Looking forward

Timothy Bear

18 five-minute stories and assembly outlines
for Advent and Christmas

Brian Sears

Acknowledgments

Timothy Bear entered my life some 35 years ago. He was a Christmas gift from a Bristol children's home which had adopted me as a family friend. Timothy Bear stories were first told to those children. Many more children have heard them since and, in many ways, allowed Timothy into their hearts. Many adults, too, have granted him a little room.

In 2006, BRF took Timothy Bear on board their good ship *Barnabas*, and fresh vistas opened up. That BRF have come back for a second helping has given Timothy and me enormous pleasure.

The songs suggested in this book have come from Linda Mayne (Burgess Hill) and Jill Weaver (Chorleywood). Children in both those areas are so fortunate to have such inspirational teachers.

I am indebted once again to my family, who support me totally: our daughters Jennifer and Katherine (even if Katherine shows a much greater attachment to Winnie the Pooh!), and Ros, my wife, whose special keyboard skills bring Timothy to his wider public.

Many of the stories in this book received their first airing at two Croxley Green schools: Little Green and Malvern Way. For the welcome, attentiveness and encouragement of staff and children at those schools, Timothy and his author are most grateful.

Brian Sears is a trained teacher with nearly 40 years' experience of primary education. He was head teacher at Yorke Mead School, Croxley Green, Hertfordshire from 1980 until his early retirement in 1997 and now continues teaching in one-to-one private tuition.

In 1984 Brian had six stories published by NCEC in an anthology, A Yearful of Stories, and has contributed to the SU Bible reading notes, Snapshots, for primary school-aged children. For the last eleven football seasons, Brian has realised his other passion in that he has written a weekly column in The Independent based on statistics of Premiership football. Eight years ago, Scripture Union and CPO jointly published Brian's record of Christians working in the football industry, Goal! Winning, Losing and Life, the writing of which involved Brian in meeting the likes of Cyrille Regis, and a memorable visit to Old Trafford to interview Manchester United's secretary and chaplain.

Brian frequently leads church services by invitation in Hertfordshire, mainly in the Baptist tradition. He is an enthusiastic Watford FC supporter, two highlights being the play-off victory eight years ago at Wembley and telling a story about Timothy Bear at the club's annual carol service. His first book about Timothy Bear, Through the Year with Timothy Bear, was published in 2006.

Text copyright © Brian Sears 2009
Illustrations copyright © Maria Maddocks 2009
The author asserts the moral right
to be identified as the author of this work

Published by
The Bible Reading Fellowship
15 The Chambers, Vineyard
Abingdon OX14 3FE
United Kingdom
Tel: +44 (0)1865 319700
Email: enquiries@brf.org.uk
Website: www.brf.org.uk

ISBN 978 1 84101 623 8
First published 2009
10 9 8 7 6 5 4 3 2 1 0
All rights reserved

Acknowledgments
Sripture quotations are taken from the Contemporary English Version of the Bible published by
HarperCollins Publishers, copyright © 1991, 1992, 1995 American Bible Society.

A catalogue record for this book is available from the British Library

Printed in Singapore by Craft Print International Ltd

Contents

Section One: Preparing for Christmas

Section Two: Light coming into the world

Section Three: Love for the world

Section Four: The gifts of Christmas

Section Five: Food at Christmas

Section Six: Celebrating Christmas

Foreword

The search for good material for Collective Worship can sometimes seem a never-ending chore. And yet, engaging a group of children with a story, in a class or larger assembly, is one of the most rewarding experiences in the school day. These Timothy Bear stories, with their planning notes, offer a wealth of material that teachers will welcome.

The stories will prove both accessible and enjoyable for the target age group: 4 to 7-year-old children. The themes provide springboards for questioning and discussion, enabling teachers to make connections with children's own experiences. With each story there are helpful suggestions for placing the material within the context of Christian-based Collective Worship. The suggestions could easily be adapted if the stories were used in a broader religious or non-religious setting.

This set of original stories responds to a problem teachers often ponder when planning Collective Worship in the second half of the autumn term, during Advent: how to prepare for Christmas without pre-empting and spoiling the excitement of the nativity narrative when it is told at the end of term. The device Brian Sears has used is to link all the stories to the production of a nativity play. The situations in which Timothy Bear gets involved are earthed in the realities of school productions and of children's feelings: they range from the delicate matter of choosing the cast to the triumph of the final performance.

In the course of telling these 18 stories, the key themes of the nativity are expressed and a range of responses explored. The outcome will be a deeper understanding of this central Christian narrative. Timothy Bear brings a welcome freshness to the very familiar and much-loved story of Jesus' birth.

Geoff Marshall-Taylor
Formerly Executive Producer, BBC Education

*

Introduction

Telling Timothy Bear stories to children

The name of the main character in the stories in this book is Timothy Bear, but he can easily change his name to suit another storyteller or story reader. He can even change his species!

I find that actually having a teddy bear with me provides a focal point for children while they listen to the story. Normally I hold him, but on occasions I might invite him to be looked after by a member of my audience. Sometimes I might place him in a special place for a particular story (by the side of a stage, say, for the 'broom-dropping' episode before I bring him to the centre for the snowy Saturday part of the story). Some stories lend themselves to asking a volunteer child to sit at the front to become a character in that particular story (a girl could be 'Linda the lights' for example, in her story). Again, it concentrates the mind and the attention of any child who might otherwise be disposed to daydream.

I am not gifted in the ability to produce a range of voices and accents. I am sure that those having such an ability add a dimension to storytelling, but I can manage a deep gruff voice that belongs to anything said by Timothy. Children seem to enjoy listening out for such input. I have never sung a solo on any public occasion in my life, but I can get away with Timothy singing the 'Away in a manger' version in the final story. He has even received applause for his rendering of it!

Having a main character that is the same in every story allows you to add local colour to the telling or reading. Names of other characters can be used to hint at folk known to the audience. We had a minister at one time called Reverend Walker, who easily became Reverend Corker in stories that included a minister. Three schools figured in the life of our large village and one word taken from each of the names provided a fictional school to which all children could feel a sense of belonging. Adults in the audience seemed especially to enjoy these contributions. To suit my own interests, Timothy is usually dressed in the colours of our local football team, and this provides a ready means of introduction when children meet him for the first time.

My hope is that each story has a positive impact just through its telling or reading. If time is at a premium, it can be left to lodge in the imagination to allow each child to take away their own individual meaning and understanding. Stories will vary, too, in their appeal. What one child gains from a particular story will not necessarily be gained by another.

When time allows, stories may be unpacked. In an assembly, this can be done by answering a few well-thought-out questions as everyone else listens attentively to what is being said. Many children will contribute readily as they remember the story and apply it to their own situations. In this book, at the end of each story there are suggested questions that may be helpful. A session like this should be kept within the attention scope of a group as large as a whole school assembly or a whole congregation.

Follow-up can be even more valuable in a smaller group of, say, a class. It is not essential for the class teacher to have been present at the assembly or even to know the story. It is good for children to recount their own version of the story and the 'morals' they have taken from it themselves. After all, in assembly situations they will realise that stories are not told just for excitement or fun or interest (although these elements may be present) but mainly for what we can learn from them for our everyday lives.

As well as questions to check that the stories have been understood, there are suggestions for follow-up activities. Then there are questions to help children apply the stories to their own world.

The thread for the stories in this book is the production of a nativity play in a Key Stage One department as part of its Christmas activities, taking place mainly in the second half of the autumn term. No particular nativity play is suggested. These days, a whole range is available and the nativity play is often part of a larger production. The stories may be used as one-offs as they fit into the school's established programme or they may be used as a series. If told as a series, it may be helpful to provide memory joggers as the stories are told. An artefact that goes with each story might be found or made, which could be placed on or around a Christmas tree or as part of an Advent calendar.

Material is also suggested that would include each story in the context of its own assembly. Suggestions for Bible links, as well as background prayers and songs, are therefore mentioned.

— Section One —

Preparing for Christmas

*

Introduction

The three stories in this opening section set the scene for Christmas. Miss Read is pointing her class towards the nativity play that they will perform at the end of term. She has the hard task of announcing the cast and Timothy has to cope with the disappointment of not getting the part he really wanted. Even at Christmas, not everything turns out as we might hope. Timothy's concern for Claude is an example to all. (The story of Timothy as the wise man who brings gold in his church's nativity is told on page 44 of *Through the Year with Timothy Bear*, Barnabas, 2006.)

The broom-dropping story comes out of the annunciation, the traditional start for the nativity play. Mary is portrayed busy at housework and dramatically letting her broom fall to the ground when she becomes aware of her angel visitor. The story suggests that we, too, can be on the lookout for our own 'broom-dropping' moments that might come through God's gifts to us or his direct activity in our lives.

The third story in this section centres on Timothy's part in the play as the innkeeper's boy and imagines the preparations that could have been made by the boy in Bethlehem's stable. One challenge of the story is for consistent good behaviour wherever we are. The possibility of the young influencing the behaviour of older people for good is also presented and could be usefully explored. (A version containing more fantasy, which has Timothy Bear arriving in Bethlehem and encountering the innkeeper's boy, is the Advent story on page 40 of *Through the Year with Timothy Bear*.)

 Bible links

The cloak and the crown

Bible passage: Isaiah 11:1–9

Honesty and fairness will be his royal robes (v. 5).

Broom-dropping moments

Bible passage: Luke 1:26–38

One month later God sent the angel Gabriel to the town of Nazareth in Galilee with a message for a virgin named Mary (vv. 26–27).

Ready for Christmas

Bible passage: Luke 2:6–7

Mary gave birth to her firstborn son. She dressed him in baby clothes and laid him on a bed of hay, because there was no room for them in the inn (v. 7).

Recommended songs

Wind through the olive trees (*Carol Gaily Carol*, A&C Black)
Mother to be (*Off to Bethlehem*, Out of the Ark Music)
Innkeeper's song (*It's a Baby*, Out of the Ark Music)

 Suggested prayers

Help us, Lord Jesus, as we get ready for Christmas, your birthday celebration. Prepare our hearts, our homes, our schools and our world. Amen

We thank you, heavenly Father, for the angels in the Christmas story— for the way they brought your messages to Mary, Joseph, the shepherds and the wise men. Help us to listen out for messages from you. Amen

Heavenly Father, you made such detailed preparations for Jesus to be born. Help us to carefully prepare as we celebrate his birthday. Amen

The cloak and the crown

 Telling tip

If this is the first story about Timothy Bear that a group of children hears, it is a good opportunity to introduce his voice. His only direct speech comes very near the end, and the reader can underline what a significant part of the story it is by making him speak in a low, gruff voice.

Miss Read made the announcement to her class immediately after half-term.

'We're going to do a play for Christmas. Its main part will be about the birth of baby Jesus. It is called a nativity play.'

Timothy Bear's class were listening very hard indeed. You might say they were all ears! They like learning new words, and 'nativity' sounded a good new word. Timothy Bear had actually heard the word before. He had been part of his church's nativity play the year before. He had been the wise man who presented baby Jesus with gold. He still had the long flowing cloak that Mrs Bear had made for him and the shiny gold crown they had made together.

Miss Read looked round at all the bright, upturned faces of her class. She knew it would be one of the hardest things of all, to announce who she had decided would play the main parts in the play. Most of her class were keen to be actors.

'We will need lots of you to join the rest of the school as the children of Bethlehem. You will be our choir,' she said. 'But there are some particular parts to be taken in the play. Amanda, I wonder if you will be Mary the mother of Jesus.'

Amanda went pink with pleasure and nodded several times.

'And Paul,' went on Miss Read, 'you should be a good Joseph as you're good at making things.'

Paul was as surprised as the rest of the class that he had been chosen. He was not always the best behaved, but now he, too, nodded his head.

Miss Read went on to suggest children to be angels and shepherds, narrators and the innkeeper. Timothy Bear's name had not yet been mentioned. He didn't mind as he'd set his heart on being a wise man again. After all, he did have the cloak and the crown, and so many had said at church what a fine wise man he had made. He would like his gift to be the gold again, but he'd make do with the frankincense or the myrrh.

'That leaves the parts of the three wise men,' continued Miss Read. 'Claude, I'd like you to bring the gold; David, you to bring the frankincense, and Michael to look after the myrrh.'

Miss Read caught sight of Timothy Bear's earnest face covered with disappointment and it rang a bell in her memory.

'Oh, and Timothy Bear, I want you to be the innkeeper's

boy. Do you think a teddy bear can play the part of a boy?'

Timothy managed a watery smile. He felt a bit tearful but he nodded. It certainly wasn't the part he wanted. He had no idea what part an innkeeper's boy would play. But Claude had his hand up. Miss Read looked enquiringly in Claude's direction.

'I'd like to be a wise man,' said Claude quietly, 'but I don't think my mum will let me. We're having an extension built at home, and Mum's so busy, she won't have time to get me ready.'

'That is a problem, Claude,' replied Miss Read. 'We have to ask parents to see to the costumes and things like that. Yes, Timothy?'

Miss Read had spotted Timothy with his paw in the air. Perhaps he would volunteer to take Claude's place. She had wondered about Timothy being a wise man.

'I already have a cloak and a crown,' began Timothy. 'I'm sure Claude can have them.'

Miss Read clapped her hands together. Claude's face lit up with delight. He would be able to be the wise man who brings gold to Jesus, after all.

'Well done, Timothy,' exclaimed Miss Read. 'If we're all as helpful as you, this will indeed be a Christmas play to remember.'

Helping children get to grips with the story

★ What is a nativity play?
★ Which part did Timothy want to have most of all in the play?
★ Which part was he given?
★ At the end of the story, why did Miss Read say that Timothy had been most helpful?

Ways for children to express the story

★ Make a list of all the characters that you think are in the nativity play.
★ Make a crown, either to fit Timothy's head or your own head.

Helping children to own the story

★ Which part would you like to have in the play?
★ Who else in your group would make a good Mary or Joseph?
★ Why did Miss Read know it was going to be very hard to announce whom she had chosen to play the different parts?
★ Why did Claude think, to begin with, that he wouldn't be able to be a wise man? Have you ever been chosen for something and not been able to do it?

Ways for children to live out the story

★ What is it like to be given a part in a play and to perform it in front of an audience?
★ Think of a time when you felt like crying but went on bravely with a 'watery' smile.
★ Think of a time when you have been disappointed. Was there anything that you or others did that made you feel a bit better?

Broom-dropping moments

✓ Telling tip

At the start of the story, Timothy could be placed at the side of the room as if in the wings for the play. Someone could act out the story of Mary with her broom. Then, when the action moves to Saturday, Timothy becomes central and should be held by the storyteller.

....

Amanda was very good at playing the part of Mary, right from the first rehearsal. Even before she had her costume, she entered into the part so well that the rest of the class forgot it was Amanda and really thought she was the young girl, Mary, living two thousand years ago.

The first scene began with Mary in her little home in Nazareth. She was feeding the chickens and tidying up, and then she would take hold of a broom to sweep the floor. The audience would clearly see the angel appearing on the stage before Mary realised he was there. After all, Mary was looking down at the floor.

Mary stopped sweeping as if something had disturbed her. She looked up and she, too, saw the angel. You could see the surprise on Mary's face and her broom went crashing to the floor.

'It's a broom-dropping moment,' thought Timothy to himself as he watched from the side of the stage.

Moments later, Mary had been told she was to have a baby boy, God's Son, and she said, 'Yes, I understand. I am God's servant. Let it happen as you say.'

It was some opening scene, and Miss Read was thrilled with the way things were going. Amanda had been a very good choice. Timothy Bear thought it was a great start, too. What drama! To meet an angel! An angel with such a message! A broom-dropping moment, indeed!

The next Saturday, Timothy woke up and immediately felt strangely excited. There was a pale glow on his bedroom ceiling. He felt drawn to his window and, sure enough, he looked out on to a white world. Snow had fallen gently in the night. There was no thought now of getting back into bed. He launched himself into Mr and Mrs Bear's room.

'It's been snowing,' he gasped, waking them up. 'Please! May I get dressed and go outside?'

Mr Bear was nodding his head.

'Two jumpers, your woolly hat and boots,' said Mum.

'You might even clear the path for us,' added Dad. 'I put the broom in the porch last night, just in case, when I saw the forecast.'

'Certainly,' shouted Timothy, already halfway down the stairs.

What a morning it was! It was still so early that cars had not yet disturbed the snow in the road. Trees and shrubs looked like white umbrellas. The world was so still and so quiet. Timothy held the broom to clear the path. Then something made him look up. It was something on the whiter-than-white lawn. It was a robin. Its red breast looked brighter than usual in this white world. The robin was so close to Timothy, closer than any bird had ever been before. The surprise made Timothy drop the broom. Fortunately the snow muffled the sound of the falling broom and the robin was not put off at all. Bear and robin looked comfortably at each other and Timothy realised that the robin must be hungry. The usual food supplies for birds were buried under centimetres of snow.

'I won't be long,' whispered Timothy.

Timothy had no doubt that the robin would be there on his return, and he was right. Timothy came back with a plate of breadcrumbs and a small beaker of water. Timothy wasn't sure if birds knew they could get water from snow.

Timothy cleared the path, glancing across every so often at the robin having breakfast.

'It's another broom-dropping moment,' thought Timothy to himself, 'but I didn't expect them to happen to me.'

It wasn't quite all over. Path cleared and breakfast eaten, the robin hadn't finished with Timothy yet. Three or four times it hopped backwards and forwards over the fence into Mrs

Centurion's garden. At last Timothy got the message that he should go round as well. Perhaps it would be a good idea to clear Mrs Centurion's path. But the robin led the way through the open gate into Mrs Centurion's back garden. The robin would go no further, but by now Timothy could hear a soft miaowing coming from the shed at the end of the garden. Mrs Centurion's cat, Marmalade, must be trapped inside.

Timothy Bear went to Marmalade's rescue. Somehow the door of the shed had closed on Marmalade the evening before and she had been imprisoned. She was only too willing to be cradled in Timothy's paws after he pulled open the door. Bear and cat made their way to the back door. Mrs Centurion came to the door in her dressing-gown. Her worried face broke into smiles as she was reunited with Marmalade.

'I was just wondering what had happened to her,' she said. 'Timothy Bear, you're an angel.'

If Timothy had been holding his broom, he would have dropped it! An angel! He modestly looked round to give the robin the credit, but the robin had flown away.

Helping children get to grips with the story

★ Why do you think Mary dropped her broom when she was cleaning her home?
★ What surprised Timothy when he woke up on the Saturday morning?
★ Why do you think Timothy dropped his broom when he was clearing the garden path?
★ What happened to Marmalade at the end of the story?

Ways for children to express the story

★ Make a broom from card or other materials.
★ Create a snowy picture.
★ Make a robin from card and colour it in.

Helping children to own the story

★ If it was a time of snow, what would you like to do out in the snow?
★ Share stories about animals being rescued.

Ways for children to live out the story

★ Timothy was surprised to have broom-dropping moments happen to him. Think of broom-dropping moments that have happened to you.
★ Mrs Centurion was so grateful to Timothy for rescuing her cat. Think of a recent moment when you have been grateful for the help someone else has given to you.
★ Think of times when someone has been grateful to you for help you have given them.

Ready for Christmas

✔ Telling tip

The story may be introduced by talking about being tidy. What tidying jobs are the children asked to do at home or at school? A black sack could be shown to aid discussion.

Early on in the nativity play practices, Miss Read made it clear to Timothy Bear that she expected him to make sure all the props for the play were in the right place and that the stage and hall were kept tidy.

'You're on the stage all the time when the play moves on to Bethlehem, so you're the ideal person.'

Timothy understood that he would know where everything should be, but he wasn't sure he was ideal. He had a reputation for untidiness and forgetfulness.

'I think the innkeeper's boy in Bethlehem must have had a lot of tidying up to do before the first Christmas,' Miss Read went on with a smile.

Timothy Bear thought hard about what it would have been like in that Bethlehem stable—draughts to be blocked out, new straw needed on the floor, the wobbly leg on the manger

24

to be made less wobbly... The innkeeper's boy must have been kept very busy indeed, even before the donkey and Mary and Joseph arrived. Perhaps the boy had not been the tidiest of people at first; perhaps he had tried to improve.

Timothy decided to do his very best to keep the school hall and stage tidy and the scenery in tiptop condition. It was quite a job. Every time the play was rehearsed, Mary scattered corn for the chickens to eat, so it all had to be swept up afterwards and the floor made spotless. The gifts from the three wise men had to be put back on the shelf at the back of the hall so that the wise men could bring them forward at the next practice. There was a whole list of things for Timothy to check. He had to give up some of his playtimes to make sure everything was done.

Miss Read mentioned to Mrs Bear how well Timothy was looking after things, one day at the end of school.

'He's so tidy and so good at remembering,' reported Miss Read.

Mrs Bear was pleased to hear her cub being praised but, without thinking, she said, 'It's a shame he can't be like that in his bedroom. I nearly fell over and twisted my paw this morning, crossing the floor to find his dirty washing. It's a tip!'

'Oh dear, Timothy,' said a smiling Miss Read. 'It sounds as if the innkeeper's boy needs to get ready for Christmas at home just as well as he's getting ready at school.'

When he arrived home and went into his bedroom, Timothy looked at it with the eyes of the innkeeper's boy. What a mess it truly was! He would not like to have visitors in there. Not even a baby donkey would find any space, and it would be far too dangerous for a baby boy.

'I'm going to be busy,' Timothy called downstairs.

And busy he certainly was. Toys and games were put carefully in their right cupboards. Clean clothes were put in his small wardrobe; dirty clothes were put in the basket that Mrs Bear had provided. A black sack that he found was packed with all the rubbish. After about an hour, Mrs Bear came to see what Timothy was up to. She clapped her paws.

'What a transformation!' she enthused. 'I'd forgotten you have this lovely blue carpet!'

Mr Bear and Timothy's sister Teresa were called up to inspect Timothy's new-look room. They were amazed at the improvement.

'I think this calls for a special ice cream and honey sauce celebration,' announced Mr Bear.

Timothy grinned with pleasure. It was often the way the family celebrated.

When the ice cream and honey was all eaten up, Timothy was in for some more surprises.

Mrs Bear said, 'My saucepan cupboard is in such a mess. I've decided I'm going to tidy it up, ready for all the Christmas food I'll be cooking.'

Teresa was not to be left out.

'My toy cupboard needs sorting out so that there's room for any new things I might get!'

Mr Bear smiled. 'And I'll clear out the loft, just in case I need to hide one or two things up there before Christmas morning.' He had his most mysterious look on his face.

'Well,' said Timothy Bear, 'the stable at Bethlehem was ready for the first Christmas and it looks as if our house, too, will be ready to celebrate Jesus' birthday when it comes this year.'

Helping children get to grips with the story

★ What important job did Miss Read give to Timothy in addition to being the innkeeper's boy?
★ Why was Mrs Bear pleased to hear that Timothy was being so tidy at school?
★ Why was Mrs Bear also surprised to hear that he was being so tidy at school?
★ What surprises did Timothy's family have for him at the end of the story?

Ways for children to express the story

★ Draw two pictures, the first of a messy bedroom and the second of a tidy bedroom.
★ Make a list for Timothy of things he might have to check up about for the nativity play.
★ Make a teddy bear-sized wastepaper basket to help Timothy keep tidy.

Helping children to own the story

★ How might the innkeeper's boy have prepared the stable for the first Christmas in Bethlehem?
★ What untidy places in our world could do with a tidy-up?
★ How would you stop people dropping litter?

★ What would you most like grown-ups at home to know about what you do in school? Is there anything you wouldn't like them to know?

Ways for children to live out the story

★ What untidy place could you do something about? Don't forget to actually do it!
★ What preparations can you make to get ready for Christmas?
★ Think of things you do that you wish others—even grown-ups—might copy.

Light coming into the world

Introduction

The first story of this second section is about the discovery of a special stone (with a hole right through its middle) that Timothy finds on holiday, months before the nativity play. Timothy's creative imagination enables him to use his collection of similar stones to settle the restless shepherds as the nativity play approaches. The story reminds us of the wholeness of life—that past experiences can be remembered and be of value a long time afterwards.

Linda's story is one to help especially those of us who have much to contribute to life in the background but shy away from leading roles. (In an actual play, it would be important for Linda to have a special mention when the rest of the class were being applauded for their 'up front' parts.) Amanda had found it easy to poke fun at shy, unresponsive Linda but in the end even she realises that Linda has abilities that are missing in her own make-up. Miss Read also has good reason to be grateful that Linda 'notices things'.

The third story attempts to tackle those times in life when we feel 'out of sorts' with ourselves and everybody else—when we are disappointed with our own behaviour or we feel something of an outcast, like the shepherds of Bethlehem 2000 years ago. God spoke into the shepherds' situation, and Timothy's.

 Bible links

First light

Bible passage: John 8:12

Jesus said, 'I am the light for the world! Follow me, and you won't be walking in the dark. You will have the light that gives life.'

Linda the lights

Bible passage: John 1:1–14

The true light that shines on everyone was coming into the world (v. 9).

Dazzling lights

Bible passage: Luke 2:8–20

All at once an angel came down to them from the Lord, and the brightness of the Lord's glory flashed around them (v. 9).

 Recommended songs

Sleepy shepherd (*The Sleepy Shepherd*, Out of the Ark Music)
Stars' song (*Witnesses*, Out of the Ark Music)
Angels' song (*Witnesses*, Out of the Ark Music)

 Suggested prayers

God who made the earth, the air, the sky, the sea; who gave the light its birth, careth for me.
SARAH RHODES

May the Lord Jesus who is the splendour of the everlasting light drive from our hearts all darkness. Amen
TRADITIONAL BLESSING

All glory be to God on high, and to the earth be peace; good-will henceforth from heaven to men, begin and never cease.
NAHUM TATE

First light

If a stone like the one in the story is available, it could be shown and discussed before the story is read.

Miss Read was having trouble with the shepherds. She had chosen five children who she thought would make good shepherds but, as it turned out, they were not good at waiting patiently. They were such fidgets. They even picked away at the green plastic grass on which they sat, and they couldn't control their crooks properly. The result was that when the extra lights suddenly came on with the appearance of the angels, the shepherds were all over the place and in no way ready to look amazed and awestruck.

'I don't know what I'm going to do with you shepherds,' complained Miss Read at the third rehearsal. 'Why can't you be more like proper shepherds?'

'What about giving us thick sticks so we can fight off wild animals?' wondered Josh, who had a thing about weapons.

'You have enough trouble looking after your crooks,' pointed out Miss Read.

'Shepherds were skilled with their slings, too,' went on Josh.

Miss Read shook her head firmly. 'We're certainly not going to risk you shepherds having stones to sling around.'

Even the shepherds had to agree with Miss Read about that.

But Timothy Bear was in the middle of a brainwave. He would tell Miss Read about it at playtime. Timothy was remembering a wonderful day in their family holiday by the sea. Mr Bear had challenged Timothy to go with him on an early morning walk to the next bay along from the one near to their caravan park. Timothy had been delighted.

Father and cub were up before sunrise. The sun actually appeared on the horizon as they began their walk. Nature, too, seemed to be waking up around them. A rabbit peeped at Timothy over the cliff top. The sunrise was awesome, spine-tingling. It made your fur stand on end.

When they reached the bay, it was a huge pebble beach.

'There must be millions of pebbles,' thought Timothy. 'Perhaps billions.'

Mr Bear and Timothy crunched their way back towards their bay. One pebble caught Timothy's eye. He had never seen one quite like it before. It was the shape of a giant polo mint or a small doughnut with a hole right through its middle. Timothy picked it up.

'Keep that in your pocket,' said Mr Bear. 'I've got an idea it will come in useful later this morning, when we go to the quay where the boats come in.'

Timothy didn't understand what his father was up to, but knew him well enough to look forward to the surprise to come. While they were getting breakfast ready, Timothy noticed Mr Bear putting the rind from the bacon into a plastic bag. He also put a ball of string in with it.

'Don't forget your special pebble,' said Mr Bear to Timothy as the family left for the quayside. 'And we must stop at the shop and buy the biggest bucket they've got.'

Half an hour later, the whole family were enjoying Mr Bear's secret. It was a crabbing expedition. Timothy and Teresa sat next to each other on the quayside with string dangling over the edge, weighted down by the special stone with the hole through the middle. Bacon rind was tied to the end of the string deep in the water. Every so often, Timothy and Teresa would feel tugs and tremors on the string and, with great patience, would reel it in to find a crab helping itself to a bacon breakfast. In all, they caught 13 crabs in their bucket. When it was time to go, Timothy tossed them all back into their watery home. 'What a wonderful, wonderful morning,' Timothy had thought.

During the rest of the holiday, Timothy made a collection of stones with holes through them. He still had them at home. Now, the problem with the shepherds at school had brought those stones to Timothy's mind. What if Miss Read tied one of his stones firmly and safely to the string of each sling so that the shepherds could pretend to fire them at wild animals? At playtime, Miss Read was thrilled with Timothy's plan and, when she mentioned it to the shepherds, they were thrilled as well. What a trick it would be when all their parents were sitting in the audience.

'But,' pointed out Miss Read, 'it will all depend on how

well you practise the rest of the play. If you're always ready to be shocked and amazed when the dazzling angels light up the stage, then we'll see about Timothy's special stones for the actual performances.'

The shepherds were transformed. At every rehearsal from then on, they were the best-behaved shepherds the school had ever known.

Helping children get to grips with the story

★ Why was Miss Read upset with her shepherds?
★ Why did the mention of shepherds' slings remind Timothy of what he had brought home with him from holiday?
★ Why did Mr Bear collect together Timothy's special stone, bacon rind, a ball of string and a big bucket?
★ What was the trick that the shepherds were going to be allowed to use in the nativity play?

Ways for children to express the story

★ Try to find some stones that have holes right through them. Alternatively, card or clay ones could be made.
★ Create an early morning picture. How will we know it is early morning?

Helping children to own the story

★ Talk about the way shepherds used slings and crooks.
★ What things do you think Timothy enjoyed about the early morning walk with Mr Bear?
★ What is easy and what is hard about crabbing?

Ways for children to live out the story

★ Think of a time when you have fidgeted. What makes us fidget?
★ Share a memory of one of your favourite times on holiday.
★ What things do you have that remind you about special times in your life?

Linda the lights

The story could be introduced by putting a few things deliberately out of place in the hall or classroom and asking the children if they can spot what is amiss.

Miss Read was worried about Linda in her class. She was so shy and so quiet; she hardly said a word, even when some children made fun of her for being so quiet. Amanda was often the ringleader in the teasing but even Timothy Bear had joined in poking fun. Even then, Linda just looked sad and said nothing. Mrs Fletcher told Miss Read it had been the same when Linda was in her class. Mrs Fletcher had discussed it with Linda's mum.

'She's quiet at home as well,' Mum had agreed, 'but she notices things and she's brilliant at finding lost things. "Linda the light" we call her.'

Miss Read had no idea what Linda could do in the nativity play—until a friend of the school whom they called Mr Mac (he was a Scotsman whose real name was Mr Macnamara) promised to loan the school a number of spotlights to make the hall more like a theatre for Christmas plays.

'They'll need a good young operator,' pointed out Mr Mac, 'someone to switch them on and off just at the right times. They come with a board that has eight switches on it.'

Immediately Miss Read thought back to her staffroom conversation with Mrs Fletcher. 'Linda the light' could surely become 'Linda the lights'. So Linda sat at the side of the hall, script in hand, switching lights on or off at just the right moments. When the angels came on, every switch was in its 'on' position to give the brightest light possible. That was easy. But Linda's favourite moment in the play was when Mary, in the darkened stable, placed the wrapped-up baby Jesus in the feeding trough. Just at that moment, Linda would switch on the single spotlight that bathed the manger in its golden glow to indicate the presence of Jesus.

'Jesus is the light himself,' thought 'Linda the lights'.

Linda, just like her mother had said, was good at noticing things. She began to put things right as well. She spotted that Mary's broom was in the wrong place and held it out for Amanda to collect. Linda also realised when Amanda forgot what she had to say back to the angel. Linda whispered what Amanda should be saying from her script so that hardly anyone realised Amanda had hesitated. It didn't occur to Linda to try to get her own back for all the times Amanda had been nasty to her in the playground. Linda noticed, too, when two of the wise men had their socks untidily about their ankles after their game of football.

'Pull your socks up,' she whispered as they were getting ready to pick up their gifts.

One afternoon, Miss Read said that they would have circle time before their rehearsal. Circle time was a chance for members of the class to talk over things that were on their minds. This afternoon Linda put her hand up to be passed the shell. When you held the shell, it was your turn to speak. Linda had never spoken in circle time before. Everyone was surprised, including Miss Read. Amanda did just wonder if Linda would tell everyone how horrid she could be. It crossed Timothy Bear's mind that he might be in trouble.

'I just think our last play rehearsal was a bit dull,' said Linda. 'We've stopped doing our best.'

'How can we improve it?' asked Miss Read. She remembered thinking that the last rehearsal had been a bit ordinary.

'Well,' continued Linda slowly, 'I'm going to imagine that someone special is watching us. For me it will be Mr Mack.'

Timothy put up his paw and was passed the shell.

'I'll pretend my mum is watching.'

Amanda put her hand up.

'I shall think of baby Jesus being alive and kicking in the manger,' she said.

Everyone smiled with pleasure.

'That's lovely,' concluded Miss Read. 'Let's go for our next rehearsal now.'

Linda noticed that Miss Read was walking more slowly than usual, and when she sat on her chair in the hall she flopped a bit and looked very pale. While everyone else was getting to their places, Linda went to Miss Bridge's room.

'I don't think Miss Read's very well,' blurted out Linda. Miss Bridge came at once and talked quietly with Miss Read. Miss Bridge clapped her hands together for all the class to listen.

'Miss Read has been so busy, she hasn't had time to eat anything all day. Linda, you see your teacher safely to the staff room, and then I will have the treat of seeing how your play is coming along.'

So now there would be a real 'special' person watching their rehearsal as well as all the pretend ones: their head teacher would be in the hall. 'Linda the lights' took her place in front of the switches. Miss Read, eating her ham rolls and then her toffee yogurt in the staff room, was grateful that Linda noticed so much. Miss Bridge was grateful, too, that Linda was telling people more of what she was noticing, and Amanda gave Linda her best friendly smile.

Helping children get to grips with the story

★ At the start of the story, why was Miss Read worried about Linda?
★ What was Linda's favourite part in the whole of the nativity play?
★ What other things did Linda notice? There are at least five things mentioned in the story.

Ways for children to express the story

★ Draw pictures in a widening beam of light. Perhaps the paper could be cut in the shape of a widening beam.
★ Draw or make a picture of a wise man with untidy socks.

Helping children to own the story

★ How do you think Linda felt when she was put in charge of the lights?
★ What was Linda's own answer to the problem that the rehearsals were getting dull?
★ Why did Linda go to Miss Bridge, and how do you think she felt about doing that?

Ways for children to live out the story

★ Are you good at noticing things? Can you think of something you've noticed and pointed out to someone else?
★ Mr Mac is a friend to Timothy's school. Who are similar friends to your school or group?
★ Linda thought, 'Jesus is the light himself.' What could Linda have meant by that?

Dazzling lights

One of the many high points of the nativity play was when the angels had gathered to one side of the stage. A spotlight picked out Barbara Pole, who had been chosen to deliver the message to the shepherds about the wonderful birth in Bethlehem's stable. Then, as the shepherds stood spellbound, every light came fully on and half of the angels proclaimed, 'Praise God in heaven!' and the other half added, 'Peace on earth to everyone who pleases God.' Then the whole school sang the angels' song before the shepherds were left in the dark to decide what to do.

But Timothy Bear, for once, at this rehearsal, did not join in with the singing in his wholehearted way. The day was not turning out gloriously for Timothy. He did not feel peaceful. It had been an unsettled and unsettling day, right from the start. Timothy had been slow getting ready for school—so slow that in the end he had made Mrs Bear cross. At play-time, he'd ganged up with others in his class to make fun of a girl called Alex, saying she had a boy's name. They went much too far and even made Alex cry. Fortunately for Timothy, Alex didn't mention his name to their head teacher when Miss Bridge came to sort things out, but Timothy knew he was partly to blame. So there had been little praise on the playground, and no peace at all.

After play, there was the nativity rehearsal, and Timothy had forgotten to make sure that Mary's broom was in its right place for Amanda. For once, it put Amanda off and she was a bit flustered. Timothy went on feeling unsettled.

In the afternoon, Miss Read was out on a course and Timothy knew he wasn't trying as hard as he could with the picture that the new teacher was asking the class to make. Praise? Peace? They were nowhere to be seen!

Home time was not the usual joyful experience. Timothy didn't notice how busy his mum was in getting ahead with the Christmas cooking.

'Timothy, could you sort out the clean clothes in the airing cupboard, please. They need to be sorted into piles for each one of us.' Why was it always him who was landed with jobs to do? Hadn't Teresa got paws as well? Timothy was too upset to notice that his paws hadn't been cleaned from his picture-making at school, so you might guess what the clothes looked like in their wobbly piles!

Just as Timothy thought he had done enough clothes sorting, Teresa came bouncing in to ask her brother to play a game with her.

'Certainly not!' burst out Timothy. 'I'm light years ahead of you at every game on the planet.'

Timothy hadn't seen Mrs Bear standing outside the open door on the landing. She heard Timothy's loud voice, saw the crumbling face of Teresa and the messy, untidy piles of her laundry.

'Timothy,' she said in her stern voice, 'you'd better have some time out under the stairs.'

Mrs Bear and Timothy both knew that this was a signal for Timothy to sort himself out. Under the stairs was a small cupboard with enough space for Timothy to sit. Usually it was a favourite place, but this evening it seemed dark and dusty.

No praise at all! What a mess he'd made of things. But what had the man said in church last week? Times to say sorry? Times for new starts? Time for baby Jesus to grow into Jesus the Saviour and offer forgiveness? Timothy was indeed very sorry for all he'd made go wrong. The angel had spoken to the shepherds about a Saviour in the stable. It was still dark under the stairs but it was as if a little light began to shine right inside Timothy Bear, and with it came some peace. He would say how sorry he was to Teresa and Mrs Bear. Tomorrow he'd make it up with Alex as well.

The light and peace grew inside him and he remembered the words of the angels at the beginning of their song. This time, deep under the stairs, Timothy sang it out wholeheartedly. 'Praise God in heaven! Peace on earth to everyone who pleases God.'

Helping children get to grips with the story

★ What was the message the angels sang at the first Christmas?
★ Why, on this particular day, did Timothy feel he could not join in wholeheartedly with the angels' song?
★ What things went wrong for Timothy when he arrived home from school that day?
★ What happened to Timothy as he sat in his cupboard under the stairs?

Ways for children to express the story

★ Draw a picture of an angel.
★ Cut out some card or paper clothes and put messy paw marks all over them.

Helping children to own the story

★ What did Timothy feel like when he knew he wasn't doing his best?
★ How do you know from the story that Timothy sometimes enjoys being just on his own? Why didn't he enjoy it on this particular day after school?

Ways for children to live out the story

★ Think quietly about times you have felt 'out of sorts' because you've let yourself down or been unkind to someone else. Tell others about it if you want to.

★ How do grown-ups let you know if you are spoiling something?
★ How does it feel when wrong things are put right?

Love for the world

Introduction

The theme of sharing friendship is basic to Christmas and the Christmas story. God shares himself in the gift of Jesus. The angels declared to the shepherds that the good news will be for everyone. Those shepherds were the first to spread the word.

In 'Friends!' Timothy learns that the scope for friendship in his classroom is wider than he first thought. In 'Sleeping rough', that scope for friendship and care is widened far beyond the classroom. In 'The black sheep and the final angel', the promise of relationship and friendship with God is presented for everyone, even when we feel we don't deserve it.

 Bible links

Friends!

Bible passage: Matthew 5:43—6:4

'If you greet only your friends, what's so great about that? ... You must always act like your Father in heaven' (vv. 47–48).

Sleeping rough

Bible passage: Luke 2:1–20

Joseph had to leave Nazareth in Galilee and go to Bethlehem in Judea... Mary was engaged to Joseph and travelled with him to Bethlehem (vv. 4–5).

The black sheep and the final angel

Bible passage: Luke 15:1–7

'If any of you has a hundred sheep, and one of them gets lost, what will you do?' (v. 4).

 ## Recommended songs

Whoops-a-daisy angel (*Whoops-a-Daisy Angel*, Out of the Ark Music)
Knock-knock-knock at the door (*It's a Baby*, Out of the Ark Music)
No room at the inn (*Songs for Every Christmas*, Out of the Ark Music)
Would you like to come along? (*The Sleepy Shepherd*, Out of the Ark Music)
Shepherd's dance (*Off to Bethlehem*, Out of the Ark Music)
There isn't any room (Rat-a-tat-tat) (*Carol Gaily Carol*, A&C Black)

 ## Suggested prayers

Help us, Lord Jesus, always to be on the lookout to increase the circle of our friends and to increase the number of those for whom we care. Amen

Lord Jesus, we thank you for the comfort we have in our lives at home, at school and in other places where we go. We remember those who are sleeping rough, those who are hungry and those who are ill. We pray for all those who are uncomfortable in our world. Amen

Lord Jesus, you love the whole world. You love everyone and everything in it. As we thank you for the love and care given to us, may we share that love and care with others. Amen

Friends!

Telling tip

A plain piece of A4 paper could clearly indicate the change from landscape to portrait when it comes in the story.

....

Nativity play rehearsals were going really well. Miss Read was delighted with her class for all that they were doing in them. The only trouble was that they were getting noisier in class—all chatter and not enough work.

'If you're not quieter, I'll have to do something about it,' she warned.

There was so much to talk about. Timothy Bear sat next to Claude and they were just as bad as everyone else. Sometimes they would get so carried away that in the middle of class they would hit hand against paw in the air and call out 'Friends'. In the end, Miss Read had had enough and on Monday morning she put her plan into action.

'I'm changing our seating arrangements,' she announced. 'From now on we'll be sitting girl, boy, girl, boy.' The news was greeted with shocked silence.

'That's more like it,' smiled Miss Read. Timothy was now

seated next to Lauren instead of Claude, and Claude was over by the window. Lauren! Timothy didn't know much about Lauren except that she was one of the angels in their play and could sing quite well. Timothy turned himself away at a slight angle when Lauren took up her new place. There would be as little contact as possible. Lauren, too, was quite happy about that.

Certainly the whole class was much quieter. Miss Read knew some were upset but she reckoned her plan was working. Timothy complained about the new seating arrangements at home, but Mrs Bear sided with Miss Read.

'Miss Read always has a good reason for what she does,' said Mum. 'The play is doing you a lot of good as well.'

As the school week went by, Timothy did notice one more thing about Lauren. He couldn't help it. Whenever there were spare moments, Lauren would be at work in her small notebook. She was filling it with drawings of other girls in the class, and they were good. Just by glancing, Timothy could tell who Lauren was drawing, and each portrait took a very few moments. Timothy couldn't draw to save his life!

By Friday afternoon, Miss Read knew that the class had had a very good week. The rehearsals were still going splendidly— the one that morning had been brilliant—and in the classroom more work was being done in a quieter atmosphere. Miss Read decided to give over the whole afternoon to picture-making, as a treat. She was keen for her class to think about which way round they should place their pieces of paper. She explained that the different ways could be called 'landscape' and 'portrait'. She suggested that they should draw one of each kind from the Christmas story to establish the names in their minds.

'I find it easier to draw a landscape,' she admitted.

Swiftly she placed a wide piece of paper on her easel and sketched in lines that soon looked like hills around Bethlehem with a stable in the distance.

Then she put a new piece of paper on the easel and turned it round so that it was taller and thinner.

'But I'm hopeless at portraits. I can't draw people very well at all.'

Timothy's paw shot up before he'd had time to think.

'Lauren could draw you a portrait. She's brilliant at them.'

Miss Read smiled.

'What a recommendation, Timothy. Come on, Lauren. You have a go, please, on my board.'

Lauren shyly went to the board with the portrait-shaped paper pinned to it. Miss Read handed Lauren her pens.

'Perhaps you could draw Timothy's portrait for us,' said Miss Read. 'He's a very handsome member of our class.'

Several children giggled but then sat in wonder as, with a few confident lines, Lauren created Timothy's likeness on the paper. After a couple of minutes, it was definitely Timothy staring out at the class.

'That certainly is our innkeeper's boy,' proclaimed Miss Read, leading the class in clapping hands as a thank you.

Lauren returned to her place amid the round of applause. Without thinking, Timothy raised his paws and exchanged 'high fives' with Lauren.

'Friends,' they both said at the same time.

Helping children get to grips with the story

★ What was the only trouble with Miss Read's class and how did Miss Read put it right?
★ What did Timothy find out about Lauren that surprised him?
★ What treat did Miss Read give her class at the end of the week?

Ways for children to express the story

★ Make a landscape picture.
★ Make a portrait picture.
★ Make a picture that comes from the nativity play.

Helping children to own the story

★ What reasons would Timothy have given for having as little contact with Lauren as possible?
★ What reasons would Timothy have given for having as much contact with Claude as possible?
★ In what ways had Timothy changed by the end of the story?

Ways for children to live out the story

★ How would you arrange for a noisy group of children to be quieter?
★ Who are the best artists that you know of your age?
★ What would you like your teacher to get you to do on your own in front of a whole class?
★ In what ways could you increase the number of friends you have?

Sleeping rough

✔ Telling tip

A red woolly bobble hat, or an invitation card to the nativity play, would be suitable props for the storytelling. It might also be advisable to set up the story by talking to the children about stranger danger and pointing out that Timothy Bear was with his dad when they approached the homeless man.

Timothy Bear saw the man stretched out asleep on the bench in the recreation ground. Timothy was going there with Mr Bear to practise his football. The man was wearing a woolly red bobble hat.

'Why on earth is he sleeping there?' Timothy wanted to know.

'He could be homeless,' answered Mr Bear. 'Quite a few people are sleeping rough these days.'

Timothy thought of his warm bed. 'I suppose I sleep smooth,' he said quietly.

The man had reminded Timothy of one of the characters in his earliest reading book at school. He had worn a red hat, too. 'I shall call him Roger Red Hat,' thought Timothy to himself.

The next time Timothy's class rehearsed the nativity play, Roger Red Hat popped into Timothy's mind. 'Would he even now be sleeping on the bench?' he wondered. But in the play Timothy was going with the innkeeper to the door of the inn. Joseph had knocked on it. It occurred to Timothy that Joseph and Mary were homeless in Bethlehem and about to sleep rough on a stable floor. The shepherds, too, were sleeping rough on the hills around Bethlehem.

There were lots of people like Roger Red Hat in the Christmas story! The wise men and the angels were a long way from their homes. Last of all, there was baby Jesus. Where was his home? And wasn't that feeding trough an uncomfortable place for a baby to sleep? It's a good job that, as the innkeeper's boy, Timothy was keeping an eye on the manger's wobbly leg.

That afternoon, Miss Read needed the help of her class on another matter. Every year they sold tickets for parents and friends to come to the Christmas play and then gave the money away to help others.

'Has anyone any idea about what the money should be used for this year?' Miss Read asked.

Immediately Timothy thought of Roger Red Hat and his paw was up like a rocket.

'Yes, Timothy,' smiled Miss Read.

'There was a lot of homelessness and sleeping rough at Bethlehem for the first Christmas,' started Timothy in what, for him, was a long speech. 'Could we help those who are still homeless round here?'

'What a fantastic idea,' said Miss Read. 'There's a charity

just started called "New Hope" that's setting out to help just those people.'

Now several hands were up, and people were making additional suggestions. In the end, as well as the money from tickets going to 'New Hope', it was agreed that Miss Bridge would try to get lists of names so that they could invite homeless people and those sleeping rough to an extra performance of the play and then provide them with a tea afterwards.

The next Saturday, Timothy went with his dad again to the recreation ground. He was half hoping to spot Roger Red Hat. Indeed, there he was—not sleeping on the bench this time but sitting on it, eating a bread roll.

'Let's go and meet Roger,' said Timothy to Mr Bear.

'How do you know the gentleman's name?' queried Mr Bear.

'Oh, I don't. That's my pretend name for him.'

The man on the bench was delighted to have company. He was even more delighted when he heard the school's plans for the special performance of their Christmas play— and the tea. He could help pass round invitations to others like him without a home. Mr Bear said he was sure that Miss Bridge would like him to come into school to help with the list.

'I'm sorry,' said Mr Bear, 'but I don't know your name.'

'Roger,' said the man with the woolly red bobble hat. 'Roger Redhead.'

Timothy Bear was not surprised in the least. He'd only got the name a little bit wrong.

Not only did Roger Redhead come in to see Miss Bridge, but Miss Read also heard about him and got him to come and talk to her class about being homeless. The class asked him lots of questions and found out so much.

When it came to the special play performance and tea, Miss Bridge was able to present a cheque for £500 to 'New Hope'. The man in charge of 'New Hope' said that they planned to spend it on special meals for homeless people over Christmas. Roger Redhead was sitting next to Timothy.

'It looks like being the best Christmas I've had in years,' said Roger.

Helping children get to grips with the story

★ Why was Roger so often to be found on the bench in the recreation ground?
★ Why did Miss Read want her class's help about the money from the tickets sold for the nativity play?
★ What did happen to the money in the end?

Ways for children to express the story

★ Make a model of a comfortable bed.
★ Make a model of a bench, which would be a much more uncomfortable bed.
★ Design an invitation card to invite homeless folk to the special performance of the nativity play.

Helping children to own the story

★ Think, like Timothy did, about all the characters in the first Christmas. Where were their real homes?

★ Why did Timothy make his suggestion for how the ticket money should be used? Was it a good idea?

Ways for children to live out the story

★ What suggestions would you make for using money to help our world?

★ What kinds of people could do with their Christmas being improved?

The black sheep and the final angel

You may wish to give the sheep a special voice in the storytelling, for example by lengthening vowels where appropriate in the sheep's speech. Before telling the story, a discussion about the rare colourings of some animals would be helpful, such as albino animals, stripeless tigers and so on—leading on to black sheep.

Miss Read didn't realise it, but May had hoped to be an angel for a long, long time. May knew it was an impossibility, though. Miss Read always chose angels with long blonde hair and blue eyes. May's hair was brown and short and her eyes were hazel. May was not surprised to hear Miss Read call out her list of angels: girls with fair hair and blue eyes. No mention of May.

'We really need one more,' Miss Read pondered, surveying her class. Timothy Bear was only half attending. He certainly didn't want to be an angel! He was thinking animal thoughts and of all the animals that there might have been at the first

59

Christmas. There must have been sheep around Bethlehem— the shepherds were looking after them. He was wondering what it was really like in those fields of Bethlehem. He must have wondered very hard. He found himself floating through time and space—spinning but never dizzy, speeding but never frightened—and he landed with the slightest bump.

Timothy Bear shivered. It was much colder than in his school. It was dark, too. A wood fire glowed, a stone's throw away. Shepherds and sheep were settling down to make themselves comfortable for the long night.

One lamb, next to Timothy, was apart from the flock. She bleated a whispered welcome: 'It's good of you to come. It's nice to have company for a change.' The lamb went on to explain, 'The others leave me out; I'm different from them. They say that when I grow up I'll be a black sheep.'

'You look all white to me,' whispered Timothy in the dark.

'It doesn't show much at night,' the lamb said quietly, 'but I'm really quite grey… What on earth?!'

A bright light had appeared in the night sky. It came nearer and nearer in the growing shape of a person. The gaze of shepherds and sheep, and bear, were drawn to it, riveted.

Then a voice sang out clearly, 'Don't be afraid! I have good news for you, which will make everyone happy. This very day in King David's home town a Saviour was born for you. He is Christ the Lord. You will know who he is, because you will find him dressed in baby clothes and lying on a bed of hay.'

The voice stopped but then the whole sky was alight. An angel choir was singing, 'Praise God in heaven! Peace on earth to everyone who pleases God.'

The light faded as quickly as it had started. Shepherds and sheep, and bear, held their breath, trying to take it all in.

'Come with me,' said the lamb to Timothy. 'Let's go to Bethlehem.'

Timothy needed no second bidding. Lamb and bear scurried across the fields, racing each other, company for each other. Timothy looked back at the shepherds, who were sorting out who should stay watching the flocks and who should go down to Bethlehem. As it happened, the longer legs of the shepherds made up the ground and they all arrived at the stable together. It was just as the angel had said it would be: a man and a woman inside, gazing in wonder at the manger containing the newborn baby.

The shepherds stopped in the low doorway, awestruck. Timothy hugged the shadows but the lamb crept fearlessly up to the feeding trough. Gently her forelegs eased up on to the rim of the manger, her eyes taking in the sight of the baby so close. Baby and lamb seemed to exchange glances of love and understanding. The lamb felt she really belonged at last.

Timothy knew that his time in Bethlehem was done. A shepherd came forward to pick up the lamb with tenderness and care. Timothy was once again floating through time and space—spinning but never dizzy, speeding but never frightened—and he landed with the slightest bump.

Miss Read was still wondering about the final angel. Timothy saw May's sad, wistful face and somehow now understood.

'Perhaps May could be the final angel?' said Timothy Bear quietly. The class smiled at the way Timothy had asked. Miss Read smiled, too. 'I don't see why not. Would you like to be an angel, May?'

May didn't have to say anything. Her delight was written all over her face. As the rehearsals went by, Miss Read noticed it was May's singing in the angelic choir that kept all the other angels together and in tune.

In the end, Timothy heard his teacher say to May, 'May, you really are an angel,' and Timothy couldn't help thinking as well of a lamb who felt she belonged for the first time at the first Christmas.

Helping children get to grips with the story

★ Why was May considered unsuitable to be an angel in the nativity play?
★ Why was the lamb that Timothy met in Bethlehem sad?
★ What made all the difference to Timothy's lamb when she reached the stable?
★ What happened to May by the end of the story, and how do we know it turned out very well?

Ways for children to express the story

★ Make two model sheep, one white and one black.
★ Try to make a picture of the lamb at the manger.
★ Draw a picture of May as an angel.

Helping children to own the story

★ Describe in your own words how you think Timothy was feeling when he arrived on the fields near Bethlehem.

★ Why did the lamb's experience make Timothy suggest that May should be the final angel?

Ways for children to live out the story

★ Think about a time when you felt left out. You may want to talk about it.

★ Timothy helped May to belong in the play. How could you help someone else to belong?

★ Can you think of people who have helped you to belong?

The gifts of Christmas

*

Introduction

This fourth section is about giving and receiving and, appropriately enough, the focus moves to the gifts that the wise men brought to Jesus.

In the first story, Claude is carried away by his arrogance in being chosen as the wise man who brings gold. Timothy, who originally wanted that part for himself, shows Claude a better way.

In the second story, it is Timothy who learns about the pleasures of giving and not just the pleasures of getting. Gifts are not only to be measured by their cost in terms of money. To appreciate this, Timothy and David (the wise man who brings frankincense in the nativity play) are transported to meet up with the original wise man bringing frankincense as he journeys to Bethlehem.

Finally in this group, Michael is the wise man who will bring myrrh. This story tackles the uncomfortable side of Christmas, when undesired happenings and even tragedy can threaten to spoil that season of the year. Michael finds comfort in rehearsing the nativity play.

 Bible links

Grandma's brooch

Bible passage: Titus 2:7

Always set a good example for others.

Giving presents

Bible passage: Matthew 2:1–18

They took out their gifts of gold, frankincense, and myrrh and gave them to Jesus (v. 11b).

Goldie

Bible passage: Matthew 2:1–18

When the men went into the house and saw the child with Mary, his mother, they knelt down and worshipped him (v. 11a).

 ## Recommended songs

We three kings (Traditional)
Some wise men in their splendour (*Carol Gaily Carol*, A&C Black)

 ## Suggested prayers

Lord Jesus, we thank you for all we receive at Christmas. Help us also to think about what we might give. Amen

The wise men brought you, Lord Jesus, the best things they could. Help us to be like them. Amen

What can I give him, poor as I am?
If I were a shepherd I would give a lamb;
if I were a wise man I would do my part;
yet what I can I give him—give my heart.
CHRISTINA ROSSETTI (1830–94)

★

Grandma's brooch

✓ Telling tip

A large brooch would be a suitable prop for the storytelling. If you also have a dressing-up cloak and crown, a volunteer could be chosen to demonstrate the difference the brooch makes to the costume.

Timothy Bear had to get used to the idea of his best friend, Claude, being the wise man who would give baby Jesus gold in the school nativity play. Timothy would have liked Miss Read to have chosen him for that part. He had been that wise man at church last year. Even though he was disappointed, Timothy still agreed that his cloak and his crown from a year earlier could be altered to fit Claude. Claude's mum couldn't possibly make a costume, so again Miss Read was grateful for Timothy's help.

Claude didn't seem so grateful. He thought being a wise man gave him the right to be bossy. He said to Timothy, 'Make sure my cloak is always hung up properly on its hanger.' Then again, 'Make sure my crown is stored on the top shelf. I don't want it squashed.'

Miss Read had put Timothy in charge of keeping things tidy and in their right place, but Claude could have done some of his own tidying-up. One or two pleases wouldn't have come amiss—and whose cloak and crown were they, anyway?

Claude was the same on the playground. David was chosen to be the wise man to bring frankincense, and Michael brought the myrrh. Claude said they should be the wise men's gang. They went round giving their orders and throwing their weight about. They had no time and no room in their gang for shepherds and certainly not for an innkeeper's boy. Timothy missed having Claude as a friend.

When it came to the rehearsals, Miss Read noticed that the wise men were getting careless about their part in the play. She had said right from the beginning, 'Slowly, wise men. Heads up straight. Carry your gifts carefully.'

Gradually the wise men were becoming sloppy. They were being silly walking up to the manger from the back of the hall and travelling much too quickly.

'Claude,' she pointed out, 'you should be setting the example. You lead the others with the gold.'

But Claude sauntered up, round-shouldered, with his cloak slipping off and his crown on crooked. Miss Read was cross when she spotted that Claude was even carrying his gift behind his back. 'Claude!' she stormed. 'Slowly. Head up straight. Carefully.'

Timothy Bear remembered when he was the wise man who carried gold in church. He remembered what had helped him so much. Grandma had loaned him her lion's-head brooch to pin his cloak high up round his neck. It was brilliant. Not only did it look good but it kept his cloak in place and it made him hold his head up straight.

'It will make you as good as gold,' his grandma had said. Timothy smiled. It had worked for him. That very evening, when they visited Grandma, Timothy asked if Claude could borrow the lion's head.

'Certainly,' said Grandma. 'Does he need to be as good as gold?' she asked, smiling. Timothy smiled back. If only Grandma knew.

Early next day, Timothy found Claude in the playground. The other wise men were not around. Claude was amazed that Timothy had arranged the loan of such a special item for him.

'Grandma says it makes the wearer as good as gold,' said Timothy. Claude was shamefaced. He had let the wise man business go to his head. He realised that wise men don't have to be bossy and bigheaded.

'Thank you, Timothy,' said Claude softly. 'It's just what I need.'

Miss Read was thrilled with the wise men's contribution to that day's rehearsal. Claude set a magnificent example. He led the wise men so slowly, head held so straight, holding the gold so carefully in front of him, crown on his head so regally. David and Michael followed Claude's example. Claude then spoke his words slowly, loudly and clearly.

'Gold I bring because Jesus is king.'

'Well done, all of you,' said Miss Read as the whole cast held its finishing position, having sung 'Come and join the celebration'.

'You wise men were especially magnificent. Claude, I think it must have something to do with that lion's-head brooch you have at your neck. You were as good as gold.'

Claude smiled a great big smile. It was smiled mostly in the direction of Timothy Bear.

Helping children get to grips with the story

★ What were the disappointing things about the way Claude behaved?
★ What did Miss Read say the wise men should be like as they brought their gifts forward to the manger?
★ Why did Timothy think Grandma could help, and what did Timothy ask her to do?
★ Why was Miss Read pleased with the way Claude was behaving by the end of the story?

Ways for children to express the story

★ Make a model or picture of Grandma's brooch.
★ Draw a picture of a wise man correctly carrying a gift.

Helping children to own the story

★ What do you think about the wise men's gang in the story?
★ In what ways could Timothy have been upset by Claude's behaviour towards him?
★ In fact, Timothy did not show it if he was upset. What did he do instead?

Ways for children to live out the story

★ When people go on being unkind, how does this story suggest the situation can be put right?

★ What does it mean to be as 'good as gold'?

Giving presents

Frankincense oil can often be obtained from a chemist's or similar shop. One or two volunteers could be invited to smell the oil, but it is advisable not to place it on the skin or allow children to touch it.

For the first time in his life, Timothy Bear was thinking about the presents he would give for Christmas this year as well as the presents he hoped to get. It was his present to Grandpa that sparked it all off. On a family walk in the woods, shuffling through the fallen leaves looking for conkers, Timothy had spotted a length of wood with a bulge at one end. He'd picked it up and, in a moment of brainwave, realised it might be perfect for his grandpa as a walking stick. Mr Bear tried it out and confirmed that it was the perfect length.

'The only trouble is, it hasn't cost me anything,' said Timothy.

'It's the thought that counts,' responded Mrs Bear. 'You could always wrap it in some of your pictures.' Timothy saw the sense of that.

At school, David had a problem about his part in the nativity play. David had been chosen to be the wise man who brings frankincense to baby Jesus. It was when Timothy and David were tidying up the stage in the hall that David mentioned what was troubling him.

'But I don't know what frankincense is,' said David to Timothy. 'At first, I thought I was bringing Frankenstein.'

Timothy smiled. He had thought exactly the same.

'Sometimes,' whispered Timothy, 'if I wonder about something really hard, I get to find out what it was really like. But I've never done it with anyone else before.'

'Let's see,' said David just as quietly. 'Let's sit on this stage block and wonder.' They did just that. They must have both wondered equally hard for they found themselves floating through time and space—spinning but never dizzy, speeding but never frightened. They landed with the slightest bump, still together.

They were in some kind of camp and all was activity around them. The sun was setting over the desert. A young man was carefully placing a silver container in the side carrier bag of a well-behaved camel. The young man was not in the least surprised to be in the company of Timothy and David.

'Hello, you two,' he began. 'Seeing us off on our journey? That's good of you. The star should appear very soon.'

David, too, was taking everything in his stride.

'Please, what is it that you're storing so carefully in the camel's luggage?'

'That silver container holds the finest juice or sap from some trees of our country. It's called frankincense and when the top of the flask is removed the smell is fantastic.'

'Where are you taking it?' asked Timothy, half knowing what the answer would be.

'We're on a journey following a star to find a brand new king who has been born for everyone in the world. This king has come from God so I'm bringing my best gift to say thank you.'

'You're being very careful. It's taking you a long time,' pointed out David.

'We have a saying in our country,' smiled the young man. 'An important part of a present is in the journey to get it to the right person.'

Timothy Bear remembered his walk in the woods.

'We have a saying like that,' said Timothy. 'It's the thought that counts.'

'Isn't it a small world?' grinned the young man. 'Look—there's our star.'

Indeed, it was now dark enough and the star could be seen above where the sun had set. David and Timothy stared at the star in wonder. But their time in the desert was done. They were once again floating through time and space—spinning but never dizzy, speeding but never frightened—and they landed back on the stage block with the slightest bump, still together.

David went to the back of the hall to make sure his silver container was safe. It was a shame that it only pretended to contain that wonderful sap with the fantastic scent.

Later that evening, Timothy gathered together all his picture-making pencils and paints. He would make such pictures for his grandpa—pictures of the times they shared together. His favourite picture would be of grandpa and grandcub striding through the woods, Grandpa swinging a walking stick with a bulge at one end.

Helping children get to grips with the story

★ What idea came to Timothy on his walk in the woods?
★ Who did Timothy and David meet at the camp in the desert?
★ What did David do as soon as he and Timothy arrived back in their school hall?
★ What did Timothy do that evening?

Ways for children to express the story

★ Draw a careful picture and think of someone to give it to as a gift.
★ Make a model or draw a picture of a camel.
★ Draw a picture of Grandpa making use of Timothy's walking stick.

Helping children to own the story

★ What worried Timothy about giving the stick he'd found in the woods to his grandpa?
★ Can you now explain what frankincense is?
★ What are the two sayings from different countries that we heard in the story?

Ways for children to live out the story

★ Make a list of people you would like to give presents to. Think up presents for each person on the list that you could make for them.

★ Can you remember the presents you were given on your last birthday and who gave them to you?

Goldie

It may be advisable to take special care to set up this story sensitively, especially for children who have been recently bereaved or lost a much-loved pet.

Timothy Bear had really wanted to be a wise man in the nativity play, but not really the wise man who presented Jesus with myrrh. Somehow, myrrh sounded a sad thing to be bringing. Anyway, it was Michael whom Miss Read asked to be that wise man. She chose Michael because he is a serious-looking boy whose face rarely lights up with smiles. Miss Read explained what myrrh is.

'It's rather like frankincense,' she told her class. 'It's the gum or sap taken from a tree. It is used especially in hot countries to anoint the bodies of people who have died.'

Michael thought it was cool to be presenting myrrh.

'But why give it to a baby who has just been born?' Michael wanted to know.

'Well,' said Miss Read, 'I think it was because Jesus would

die when he was a young man, and the way that he died is still remembered all over the world.'

Nearer and nearer came the time for the public performances of this year's Christmas play. At last they were to have the dress rehearsal, when, as well as costumes being complete, Linda would be operating the lights with different coloured effects. Miss Read said they would have their dress rehearsal as late as they could in afternoon school.

'Then you'll get used to it being almost as dark as when your parents come,' she told them.

The evening before the dress rehearsal, tragedy struck Michael and his family. No one knew who had left the front gate open. Their dog, Goldie, was quite old—he was not quick enough dashing across the road, and the advancing car had no chance of avoiding him in the gathering gloom. Goldie was killed instantly. Michael and his family buried Goldie that very evening in their back garden.

'It's not fair,' groaned Michael. 'It's going to spoil Christmas. Bad things shouldn't happen near Christmas.'

Michael's dad wasn't so sure about that. He remembered what King Herod had done, the first Christmas. He told Michael that King Herod had had baby boys in Bethlehem killed by his soldiers but Jesus had just escaped. Michael didn't feel any better.

The next morning, Michael wasn't sure that he felt like going ahead with the nativity play rehearsal. His mum said he should give school a try. Michael looked even more serious than usual when he did get to school. He could only just manage to tell his friends what had happened to Goldie without crying. Michael's mum had let Miss Read know about it.

'Michael is going to do his best,' Miss Read told the class. 'Michael, you might find it helpful in the end.'

The dress rehearsal went reasonably well. There were one or two things that Miss Read reckoned would come 'right on the night' of their first performance. The three wise men made their way forward from the back of the hall—slowly, heads up straight—carefully carrying their gifts. Michael's face was not only serious but sad as well. Today, he didn't have to act the part for carrying myrrh.

Linda gradually increased the lighting in the hall as the three wise men neared the stable. Light reflected back off the silver star hanging above the stable's roof. The wise men arrived and knelt at the manger. That was the moment for Linda to turn on the switch that directed a golden beam of light right into the manger. The whole cast gasped in wonder at the golden glow that embraced the cradle of the baby Jesus.

'Goldie,' thought Michael to himself. Then it was his turn to speak as he presented his gift of myrrh. He spoke in his clearest voice: 'I bring myrrh for the king born to die, for the king that comforts us now.'

In that moment, Michael felt a special comfort just for him.

Helping children get to grips with the story

★ Why did Miss Read choose Michael to bring the myrrh?
★ What happened outside Michael's house the evening before the dress rehearsal?
★ How did Michael feel at the beginning of the dress rehearsal, and how did he feel by the end?

Ways for children to express the story

★ Draw a picture of Goldie or one of your own pets.
★ Draw a picture of the manger in a golden beam of light.

Helping children to own the story

★ What is myrrh? Why is myrrh quite a sad thing to give to a baby?
★ Why did Michael wonder if he should go to school on the day of the dress rehearsal? Was his mum right to say he should go?

Ways for children to live out the story

★ If you can, talk about a pet that you once had, who is now no longer around. How did it feel when the pet died or went missing?
★ When sad things happen, what can help us?

— Section Five —

Food at Christmas

Introduction

Food is an important item on the Christmas agenda! The first story in this section has even young Timothy facing up to his overweight problems. Tying the Key Stage One nativity play in with Key Stage Two's production of *Oliver!*, Timothy is challenged to give up sweets and honey during the run-up to Christmas. It becomes an even bigger challenge when Timothy is presented with his special Advent calendar.

Timothy's feelings of hunger feature in the second story. Timothy's class visit their local residential care home to sing the songs from the nativity play. Timothy's rumbling tummy is in danger of being an unwelcome accompaniment to the singing. Auntie Dorothy, a resident of the home, and her mince pies come to the rescue.

Finally in this section, the legend of the candy cane provides an answer when Timothy, as the innkeeper's boy, poses the question, 'Who is he?' of the baby in the manger.

 Bible links

Gruel and chocolate

Bible passage: 1 Corinthians 6:19–20

Your body is a temple where the Holy Spirit lives (v. 19).

Auntie's mince pies

Bible passage: Matthew 1:23

He will be called 'Immanuel', which means 'God is with us'.

The candy cane

Bible passage: Luke 1:31–33

'He will be great and will be called the Son of God Most High' (v. 32).

 ## Recommended songs

Christmas has started (*Songs for every Christmas*, Out of the Ark Music)
Food, glorious food (from *Oliver!*)

 ## Suggested prayers

For health and strength and daily food, we praise your name, O Lord.
TRADITIONAL GRACE

All good gifts around us are sent from heaven above.
Then thank the Lord, O thank the Lord, for all his love.
MATTHIAS CLAUDIUS

Dear God, just as Mary—when she heard she was to be the mother of Jesus—thanked you for giving hungry people good things to eat, so we too thank you for the good things you give us to eat. Amen

Gruel and chocolate

A chance for the group to pool their knowledge of Oliver Twist before the story is told would be a helpful preparation.

The older children in Timothy Bear's school were putting on a play for Christmas about a boy called Oliver Twist. Key Stage One children were invited to see a rehearsal of it at the end of November. A week later, Key Stage Two children would come to see the nativity play. Timothy knew bits about Oliver already. He knew that Oliver was an orphan who became a pickpocket for an old man called Fagin.

The play started in the orphanage with the children queuing up for their dinner. Dinner was a bowl full of weak soup called gruel. 'What a word!' thought Timothy. 'Cruel, gruel; cruel gruel.' Timothy enjoys the sounds of words but he didn't think he would enjoy the taste of gruel.

The Key Stage Two choir beautifully sang a song called 'Food, glorious food'. It was a song that imagined lots of tasty foods to compare with the gruel on offer in the orphanage. Timothy Bear's imagination ran riot with the song. 'Cold jelly and custard...' and Mrs Bear's honey crumble and ice cream. 'Pease pudding and saveloys'—Timothy had his doubts about those from the song but not about his mum's roast turkey and stuffing. 'Just picture a great big steak; just picture some Christmas cake...' He could dream about all the Christmas treats that awaited him, dreams that would become real. Mrs Bear is a good cook all year long but she excels herself at Christmas.

Timothy rubbed his tummy in anticipation—a tummy that bulged a bit too much already. Mum had already mentioned that he shouldn't become too tubby.

By this time, the gruel meal was almost over in the orphanage. The time had come for Oliver to stand up and move forward towards the large man who was in charge. 'Please, sir,' asked Oliver most politely, 'I want some more.'

How hungry he must be to want more of that gruel—more of that slimy mush!

'More?!' exploded the large man.

Timothy Bear was left wondering if some people were still around who existed on drab food like gruel. He certainly didn't, and he thought again about his tubby tummy and his need to do something about it. Then it suddenly hit him. To get ready for the delights of Christmas, he would give up sweets and honey until Christmas came. He really would.

Having made his resolution, Timothy enjoyed the rest of the Oliver play. It was a great story, so well performed. He was full of it at home that evening. Mrs Bear, too, had something to tell him.

'Have you remembered, Timothy, that December starts

tomorrow? We have something for you—one for you and one for Teresa.'

Timothy had completely forgotten that it was time for Advent calendars.

'These were the only ones left in the shop,' confessed Mrs Bear. 'I'm afraid they've got a wrapped chocolate surprise behind each picture.'

'Oh no!' sighed Timothy, paw going to his mouth. 'I've given up sweets till Christmas.' He explained what he had decided during the play at school.

'Good,' said Mrs Bear. 'I'm worried about your weight. You can keep the chocolates in Grandma's tin until you decide what to do with them.'

It was very hard but Timothy kept to his resolution. As December went by, Grandma's tin was filling up and Timothy still enjoyed looking carefully at each day's picture. So often, he was reminded of a part in their nativity play. Then he heard about the tea that was being arranged after a special performance of their play for people who were homeless in the area. Tea and biscuits were to be provided.

'A bit better than gruel,' thought Timothy, 'But what if there were chocolates, too?' Perhaps, these days, homeless people were a bit like Oliver Twist and could do with a more exciting diet. As he took Grandma's tin to school, he guessed that chocolates before Christmas would be good for homeless people, and giving his chocolates away would be good for him, too.

Helping children get to grips with the story

★ What did Timothy find out about Oliver Twist?
★ What did Timothy decide to do while he was watching the play?
★ Why did the Advent calendar cause Timothy a problem?
★ How did Timothy solve the problem?

Ways for children to express the story

★ Make up a list of words that you think sound interesting.
★ Draw at least one picture that might be in an Advent calendar. You might draw more than one, or even draw a whole calendar.

Helping children to own the story

★ What do you think are Timothy Bear's favourite foods?
★ Why do you think Timothy had become overweight?
★ Do you think Timothy did lose some weight before Christmas?

Ways for children to live out the story

★ You might be able to find out more of the Oliver Twist story. It was written over 150 years ago by a man called Charles Dickens.
★ Who can you think of today that, like the Oliver Twists of the past, does not have enough to eat?
★ What resolutions could you make for yourself in the weeks leading up to Christmas?

Auntie's mince pies

✔ Telling tip

Some mince pies stored in a big, round cake tin would make a good visual aid to the storytelling.

One of the best things about the nativity play was the quality and the volume of the singing. Those not fortunate enough to get an acting part were really throwing themselves heart and soul—and voice—into the Christmas songs and carols. Miss Read thought it was so good that she arranged to take her class on a visit to their local residential care home to sing the songs from the nativity play.

'I'll let your parents know,' announced Miss Read, 'and we'll go at the end of school, just as it's getting dark. It will be real carol singing.'

The class buzzed with excitement at the prospect. Timothy Bear was particularly excited as he realised that his Auntie Dorothy was one of the residents at the home. Mrs Bear made sure Auntie Dorothy knew about the coming visit so that she could get excited too.

When the afternoon came, it was one of the coldest days

they had had that winter. Scarves and gloves were the order of the day. Timothy was grateful as well that his fur kept him so warm, but he was feeling very hungry inside. Timothy's resolution to give up honey and sweets before Christmas was really working, but it did make him feel hungry between meals.

Miss Read gathered her class together outside the care home. They would sing a couple of songs there in the cold before giving their concert inside.

'We'll start with a quiet one,' suggested Miss Read. '"Born in the night, Mary's child"… one, two, three, four!' The class sang the song unaccompanied so very well. Timothy Bear knows that he's a bit of a growler when it comes to singing. Miss Read had even suggested in the play that he could just whisper the words of the songs! But in this quiet carol it was Timothy's hungry rumbling tummy that began to be heard. Outside in the open air, people didn't notice too much. Then Miss Read suggested they should sing 'We wish you a merry Christmas'. When they got to the verse about wanting figgy pudding, that made Timothy feel even hungrier (not that he was sure what figgy pudding would taste like).

Moments later, the class were in the spacious lounge, getting into their places. Timothy looked round at the smiling elderly faces. No Auntie Dorothy. He whispered to the kind lady who had let them in and seemed to be in charge.

'I was expecting to see my Auntie Dorothy.'

'Let's go up to her room and see what's happened,' replied the kind lady.

They rang the bell of Auntie's room. In the end, Auntie Dorothy opened the door, blinking in surprise.

'Oh dear,' she said. 'I've been asleep. 'Have I missed your concert?' Timothy shook his head.

'Wait a minute and I'll be ready.'

A minute later, Auntie Dorothy was back with a big round cake tin that she handed to the lady in charge.

'Here's what I promised,' said Auntie.

The carol concert was a great success. The class sang out and their smiling faces matched the faces of their audience. Most of the carols were songs that needed full volume and loudest voices. Timothy's rumbling tum was not noticed, but he knew that they were finishing with 'Away in a manger' and that Miss Read wanted it sung quietly and sweetly.

Before they reached the last carol, however, the kind lady in charge stood up and said how pleased everyone was that the class had come on their visit.

'As a treat,' she went on, 'Dorothy has made us some mince pies to enjoy before you bring our concert to a close. And, children, don't worry about the crumbs. My dog makes a wonderful hoover!'

Timothy Bear couldn't remember having a mince pie before, but his Auntie Dorothy had made them so they were sure to be good. They were! Timothy's mince pie was delicious and it filled the space in his tummy perfectly. Timothy remembered to whisper his way through 'Away in a manger'. His voice did not spoil the sweetness of the singing... and neither did his tummy.

Helping children get to grips with the story

★ Where did Miss Read take her class on a visit?
★ Why was Timothy especially pleased to go there?
★ What was causing Timothy's tummy to rumble?
★ Why was Auntie Dorothy missing to begin with and why was it important to the story that she came in the end?

Ways for children to express the story

★ Make a model or a picture of the scarf Timothy might have been wearing for the visit. Some children may even be able to knit one.
★ Make a list of Christmas songs that would be good to sing in a Christmas concert.

Helping children to own the story

★ Why was it a good thing for the class to visit the residential care home?
★ Why was Timothy worried about his tummy?
★ Why did Timothy think he would enjoy his mince pie even though he hadn't had one before?

Ways for children to live out the story

★ Do you know anyone who can no longer live in their own home, like Auntie Dorothy? How might you help them?
★ Think about what it might feel like to worry about spoiling something a group has been doing. You might like to talk to others about a time when this has happened to you.

The candy cane

Telling tip

It is very helpful for the storyteller to have a candy cane to illustrate this story. If the size of the group is appropriate and funding is available, the gift of a candy cane to each hearer at the end would be well received. Some candy canes have an additional green stripe, which could be used to indicate that Jesus is a gift for everyone in the whole world.

The part of the innkeeper's boy in the nativity play was a speaking part. It must have been the shortest speech on record but it was vital to the play. It came very near the end. The whole cast was assembled round the manger in Bethlehem's stable—the shepherds, the angels, the wise men, Mary and Joseph—everyone. At that moment, Timothy Bear was to step forward right next to the manger and ask loudly, slowly and clearly, 'Who is he?' Joseph would give the answer, 'He is Jesus—God's Son, our Saviour.' That was the signal for everyone to sing 'Come and join the celebration'.

It was strange that the Sunday before the performances the speaker in church asked the same question about Jesus:

'Who is he?' He said that as Christmas was such a busy time, with so much to remember, he would tell the story of a special sweet that was made to remind people about who Jesus is. Best of all, he had one of the sweets for each member of the congregation to take home with them. It would jog their memories. The speaker began his story.

'Our sweetmaker lived in America, and in America some sweets are called candy. He made a special candy cane to celebrate the birth of Jesus.'

Even though Timothy had given up sweets in the run-up to Christmas, he was fascinated by what the speaker had to say. The candy cane did indeed do its job of keeping the talk clear in Timothy's mind. He took it with him to school the next day, hoping that Miss Read would let him take part in that afternoon's 'Show and Tell' time. It worked out perfectly. For once, no other paw or hand was up in the air, only Timothy's.

'Well, the floor is yours,' smiled Miss Read, 'and there's still ten minutes of school to go.'

'Who is he?' began Timothy Bear theatrically. Many were now smiling. One or two giggled. 'This might help us remember who Jesus is,' went on Timothy, and he produced the candy cane. Timothy remembered the way the speaker of the day before had delivered his talk by asking questions. He decided on the same approach. 'What is the main colour of the candy?' Timothy pointed to Laura.

'White,' she said quietly.

'Yes, white, because Jesus is pure and good,' said Timothy. 'And what letter does this look like?' Timothy held the cane so that the curved bit was hanging down.

'J for Jesus,' said Claude.

Timothy turned the cane up the other way. 'What does it look like now?'

'My grandad's walking stick,' said Amanda.

'Not bad,' admitted Timothy, but Sanjay, one of the shepherds, had his hand up.

'It's the shape of one of our crooks that we use to keep the sheep in their place.'

Timothy nodded. It was all going rather well!

'But what about the red stripe?'

This time it was Michael, the wise man who brings myrrh, wanting to answer.

'Does the red stripe remind us that Jesus' death was going to be so important?' Again Timothy was nodding.

'There's one other thing I can remember,' went on Timothy. 'The candymaker added peppermint to remind us of the spices the wise men brought to Jesus. That's it,' finished Timothy. He had run out of things to say.

'Let's give our innkeeper's boy a clap,' said a delighted Miss Read. 'What a shame we haven't all got a candy cane to take home with us, but I have seen them in the shops, and I do like to give you a little something for Christmas. It would celebrate so much about our nativity play—it would be a sweet reminder.'

This time the class decided to give Miss Read a clap. It might encourage her to visit the shops.

Helping children get to grips with the story

★ What line did Timothy have to learn to say for the nativity play?
★ What happened in church on the Sunday, that reminded Timothy of the nativity play at school?
★ At 'Show and Tell' time, Timothy remembered five ways that the candy cane reminded him of Jesus. How many can you remember?

Ways for children to express the story

★ Make your own picture or model of a candy cane. Remember that it looks like the shape of a capital J or, the other way up, like a shepherd's crook.
★ Make a name-plate that says 'Jesus'.

Helping children to own the story

★ In the play, when Joseph is asked, 'Who is he?' he gives the answer, 'He is Jesus—God's Son, our Saviour.' What does the story of the candy cane add to that answer about Jesus?
★ Do you think Miss Read did get her class a candy cane each for Christmas?

Ways for children to live out the story

★ What object is a reminder to you of Christmas?
★ What would you say about that object if it was your turn in 'Show and Tell'?

— Section Six —

Celebrating Christmas

★

Introduction

The final section leading up to Christmas has to be one of celebration. In 'Party time', Timothy discovers the difference the first Christmas made to the animals in the stable and finds that there might even have been a party to round things off. On his way home, Timothy catches a glimpse of heavenly celebrations.

The nativity play is finally performed to parents and friends. Once more, Timothy does his best to ensure success—even if his spelling lets him down. A main lesson is what can be achieved when children and adults work together, each supporting the other.

The final story sees the conclusion of the term in Timothy's class. Miss Read arranges a class concert for the final afternoon. Timothy has excitingly discovered, through Mrs Bear's story, that there could have been one of his ancestors in Bethlehem 2000 years before. Not only does Miss Read narrate Mrs Bear's story, but Timothy also sings Mrs Bear's version of 'Away in a manger' as the final item of the concert. Christmas and the place of cuddly toys in the lives of young children are richly celebrated.

 Bible links

Party time

Bible passage: Psalm 150:6

Let every living creature praise the Lord.

The performance

Bible passage: Luke 2:1–20

Everything they had seen and heard was just as the angel had said (v. 20).

Josephus Bear

Bible passage: Matthew 2:1–15

'Get up! Hurry and take the child and his mother to Eygpt!' (v. 13).

 ## Recommended songs

It's a baby (*It's a Baby*, Out of the Ark Music)
Hallelujah (*It's a Baby*, Out of the Ark Music)
Away in a manger (Traditional)
Come and join the celebration (Traditional)

 ## Suggested prayers

Lord Jesus, we celebrate Christmas; we celebrate your birthday; praise God in heaven! Peace on earth to us all. Amen

Hope of the world, Mary's child, you're coming soon to reign.
King of the earth, Mary's child, walk in our streets again.
GEOFFREY AINGER

Be near me, Lord Jesus; I ask thee to stay
Close by me for ever, and love me, I pray.
Bless all the dear children in thy tender care,
And fit us for heaven to live with thee there.
J.T. MCFARLAND

Party time

✓ Telling tip

It is an easy task for a script to be made out for a grumpy cow, a doubtful donkey and a sad sheep. These parts can then be woven into the telling of the story. In a church situation, the scripts would work with instant volunteers, but in a school situation short preliminary rehearsals are advised.

To Timothy Bear's mind, there weren't nearly enough animals in Miss Read's nativity play. In fact, there was only one—the donkey that carried Mary all the way from Nazareth to Bethlehem.

Matthew had been given the part of the donkey. He was draped in a brown cloth, and two cricket stumps in his hands played the part of his two front legs. Only Matthew's mum in the audience would know that the donkey was indeed Matthew. But Timothy thought there must have been several animals around baby Jesus. After all, he was put in a manger and a manger must have once held food for animals. And shepherds look after sheep!

'I suppose the wise men must have come by camel,' said

Timothy to himself. 'But the camels would have been too big to enter a stable.'

Timothy wondered how the animals would have celebrated the birth of the baby in their stable. Animals love a party! Timothy must have wondered very hard. He found himself floating through time and space—spinning but never dizzy, speeding but never frightened—and he landed with the slightest bump.

It was very dark. There were strong smells. His ears were hearing confused animal conversations. Slowly his eyes grew used to his surroundings. A little starlight came through gaps in the roof. The other animals were not in the least surprised that Timothy had joined them, but there was nothing like a party going on. In fact, a cow was having her bad-tempered say.

'What a lot of fuss!' she moaned, mooing moodily. 'We can hardly move and now we've been invaded by humans. It was bad enough when there were just two of them but our feeding trough has been taken over by their human calf.'

Timothy Bear was sure he knew where he was but he was still surprised when he heard himself speaking out.

'Steady on. Don't you realise who that baby is? It's baby Jesus, born to be king.'

'Stuff and nonsense!' retorted the grumpy cow. 'A king born here?' She lowed a laugh, hard and bitter.

A donkey took over from the cow and Timothy was glad to hear that he spoke more gently.

'A king, you say? I've carried his mum a long way and she didn't seem like a princess. And kings can cause wars and fighting.'

'This king is different,' said Timothy, feeling a bit better. 'He's a king of love and peace. In fact, when he grows up he will ride into a city on a donkey to show that he comes in gentleness and not with an army of soldiers.'

'We could do with a king like that,' brayed the donkey. 'I'm going to have a closer look while they're all asleep.'

There was a sad bleat at Timothy's side.

'I'm too small for anyone to ride,' sobbed a sheep. 'I'm not much use at all.'

'Don't think like that,' said Timothy. 'When that baby grows up, he's going to tell a story about a lost sheep. The lost sheep gets found by a good shepherd. That one sheep is so special that they have a party to celebrate.'

The sad sheep had cheered up. The worried donkey came back enchanted. Even the grumpy cow had been listening carefully and was brightening up.

'Perhaps we should have a party,' she said, 'to celebrate a new life.'

'Yes,' joined in the donkey. 'I'm all for a bit of a knees-up.'

'I'll do a charade of a nursery rhyme,' said the sheep, who now felt quite special herself. She pretended to stagger across the stable with heavy loads on her back. Then she came back and did it again.

'I know,' said a calf that Timothy noticed for the first time. 'Baa, baa, black sheep.'

The sheep nodded and smiled with pleasure. Timothy took off his scarf and they played blind animal's bluff. Then it was a game of sleeping lions. They didn't want to wake the baby by making too much noise.

It seemed to Timothy that it was a good time to leave, while the stable party was in full swing. Timothy was once again floating through time and space. As he left the stable, high in the sky he caught a glimpse of a cloud of angels— and they seemed to turn for a moment, kicking their feet in the air. Perhaps they were having a knees-up, too!

Timothy was spinning but never dizzy, speeding but never frightened, and he landed with the slightest bump. There had been an animals' party to celebrate the first Christmas, after all.

Helping children get to grips with the story

★ What different animals did Timothy Bear think must have been part of the Christmas story?
★ Why was the cow in a bad mood?
★ What cheered up the sad sheep?
★ What three games are mentioned that the animals played in the stable?

Ways for children to express the story

★ Can you think of other games that would be good for an animals' party?
★ Make a model or a picture of a donkey.
★ Think of a nursery rhyme and how you would act it out without saying anything.

Helping children to own the story

★ Timothy expected to find a party going on in Bethlehem's stable, but what did he find was happening?
★ How did Timothy help the donkey to understand what kind of king Jesus would be?

Ways for children to live out the story

★ Think about what it might feel like if everyone else is being happy but you are sad. Has this ever happened to you?
★ Remember the best parties you have enjoyed.
★ What do you think would be the best ways to celebrate Jesus' birthday?

The performance

A copy of the notice that Timothy Bear made could be produced at the appropriate moment.

It was the evening of the main performance of the nativity play. It had been on the children's minds all day. Every preparation had been made that could be made, but now the class was coping with its nervousness. Even Miss Read was nervous.

'It's all part of giving our best,' said Miss Read to her tense and excited class. 'Being nervous shows that it all means a lot to us.'

Timothy Bear's first task when he came back to school was to check that everything was in order in the hall and all the props were in their right place. What he hadn't expected was that the audience was already arriving—adults, parents and friends.

How noisy they all were! Miss Bridge would never allow her school to assemble chatting and knocking into chairs. Some were even speaking on their mobile phones.

Such a restless audience would spoil the play. Timothy must do something! Miss Read was much too busy back in the classroom getting everyone ready.

There was a spare movable display board just by the door, just right for a notice that Timothy could make. He knew where there were some felt-tipped pens and a large piece of cardboard. He would ask the grown-ups on the notice to please keep their noise down and to please switch off their mobiles.

His spelling was perfect until he left the 'i' out of noise— 'Please keep your nose down,' the notice said—and he put an extra 'o' in mobiles ('moobiles'). Perhaps he had cows on his mind!

Some in the audience saw Timothy pin up his notice. Some nudged each other and smiled. Others tapped their noses and grinned. The audience was delighted; they became much quieter. Not a single mobile was left on. Everyone prepared themselves to enjoy the play.

What a play it turned out to be! Amanda set the standard with her performance as Mary. Her conversation with the angel was clear and dramatic. Joseph was so attentive and, when he brought on the donkey, the donkey almost skipped in a most amusing and undonkey-like way. The singing of 'Little donkey' set the standard for all the other songs. The audience heard every word. The innkeeper was stressed and short-tempered when Joseph knocked at his door. Timothy Bear, as the innkeeper's boy, led the couple and their donkey much more gently to the stable. 'Born in the night' was sung softly but so very sweetly.

The shepherds had their crooks and their slings. They acted the part of defending their sheep from the wild animals with great energy and then stood stock-still at the approach of the angels. The angels glided and shimmered in contrast to the rough-and-ready shepherds. They delivered their vital message about a special birth in Bethlehem in a stable. Moments later, the shepherds were arriving at that stable and finding it all just as the angels had told them. Then it was the turn of the wise men, led by Claude, setting a fine example bringing gold.

'Linda the lights' operated her switches without a single mistake and the darkness of the night did much to enhance her work. The whole cast assembled and Timothy asked his question, 'Who is he?' The answer came, that he was Jesus—God's Son, our Saviour.

The whole school launched into 'Come and join the celebration' with tuneful gusto. What a celebration, indeed! Even the audience joined in the chorus with increasing enthusiasm.

Come and join the celebration.
There's a new king born today!

The applause echoed round the hall, loud and long. Some members of the audience even stood up, making it a standing ovation. A few brushed away tears of pride and happiness. At last, Miss Bridge judged it the right moment to move forward to conclude the evening with her thanks. She was pink with pride and she had a special word for the audience.

'In all my years of being here for public performances,' she pointed out, 'I have never known a better audience. You even lifted the performance. It's a wonderful example of young and old working together.' A mum in the front row joined in. She turned the display panel round so that Miss Bridge and the school could see Timothy's notice.

'I think this had something to do with it,' said the smiling mum.

Miss Bridge smiled, too. 'I think I recognise the handwriting,' she said, and then paused. 'Or should I say the paw-writing. I do see we still have some work to do in improving our spelling.'

To everyone's enjoyment, Timothy tried to hide himself behind his paws and the audience broke into even more applause.

Helping children get to grips with the story

★ What did Timothy discover in the hall that might have spoilt the performance of the nativity play? What did he do about it?
★ What pleased Miss Bridge about the performance?
★ Why, at the end, did Timothy try to hide behind his paws?

Ways for children to express the story

★ Make a picture of Timothy's notice, including his spelling mistakes.
★ Draw a picture of your favourite part of the nativity play.

Helping children to own the story

★ In what other ways could Timothy have done something about the noise in the hall? Would any of them have been better than the way Timothy chose?
★ Why do you think some in the audience had tears in their eyes by the end of the play?

Ways for children to live out the story

★ When have you felt nervous? Do you agree with Miss Read that being nervous is part of 'giving our best'?
★ Can you remember being applauded for anything you've done? If you can, when did it happen and what did it feel like?
★ Timothy obviously needs to improve his spelling! What things might you need to improve?

Josephus Bear

Even those of us who are not very tuneful need not be shy of singing Timothy Bear's carol. It is well established by now that he's a bit of a growler, and audiences delight in the unexpected event of a storyteller turned singer.

Miss Read was thrilled with her class. The nativity play had been wonderfully performed. Now it was the end of term.

'On the last afternoon,' Miss Read told her class, 'we'll have a concert among ourselves. You might say a poem, tell a joke, sing a song or something else. I'll make a list of what you want to do.'

There were lots of volunteers. It would make a great end to the term. Last of all, Miss Read noticed Timothy Bear's paw up in the air. She nodded.

'I'll sing a carol that has a line about me in it!'

There were lots of smiles and Miss Read did wonder if it would be safe to let Timothy sing a solo. He's known to be a bit of a growler!

'What's it all about, Timothy?' wondered Miss Read.

'It's a long story,' replied Timothy, very seriously. 'I'll get my mum to write it all down. Perhaps, Miss Read, you'll read what she writes and then I'll sing the song?'

Miss Read agreed. She was half expecting not to hear any more about it, but next morning Timothy arrived at school with an envelope. When Miss Read read what was inside, she thought it would be quite safe to go ahead with the story and the song. In fact, she left it until the last item in the concert. So, just before the end of school, Miss Read began to read out aloud what Mrs Bear had written down.

'For some time Timothy has been anxious that the animals in Bethlehem should be more recognised for the part they played when Jesus was born. He even reckons there should be a bear in the story. Here's the story I've made up for him.

'A long time ago in Bethlehem there lived a toymaker. He was a very good craftsman and children liked his toys. He made rag balls, wooden soldiers and things like that. He made animal shapes out of materials and stuffed them with wood shavings and sheep's wool. One day he tried to make a bear, but it looked so real that children were frightened and didn't want it. So the toy maker threw the bear down in the corner of his workroom, where it lay forgotten. Some wood shavings escaped through a hole in its paw.

'Later, the toymaker was doing so well that he was offered an important job in the toy department of a large Jerusalem shop. He moved away, and it so happened that he rented his house to Mary, Joseph and the growing baby Jesus. They couldn't live in the stable for ever. They were grateful to have more room, anyway, and fewer draughts.

'Of course, Jesus cried a lot when his teeth started pushing through his tiny gums. Mary wondered how she could help him. One day, she spotted the forgotten bear lying in the corner and pointed him out to Joseph. "He looks a bit fierce," said Joseph. "Let me give him a kinder face and I'll put a stitch or two in that paw."

'Mary and Joseph were delighted when Jesus held the bear and gurgled with pleasure. "We will call him Josephus Bear," announced Mary, and Joseph was as pleased as punch.

'After a little while, an angel came to Joseph to say that the family must move to Egypt. Wicked King Herod was planning horrible things. So Mary and Joseph prepared for another journey, and I hope you can guess what was the first thing that they gave to Jesus to comfort him.'

Miss Read had finished what Mrs Bear had written and she paused. Many of the class softly whispered, 'Josephus Bear'. Miss Read nodded. 'And now Timothy has his carol for us. He tells me it goes to the tune of "Away in a manger".'

For the first time in his life, Timothy Bear stood up to sing to an audience, and this is what he sang.

When the baby grew older
And his first teeth came through,
Then little Lord Jesus had some crying to do.
And only Josephus could comfort him there,
So they cuddled each other, the baby and bear.

That's why all the children
Should have a bear too,

So when they need comfort, they'll know what to do.
His name will not matter, he has much love to share;
It might be Josephus or Timothy Bear.

The class burst out clapping. The concert had come to a good conclusion. It was time to go home and Christmas was just around the corner.

Helping children get to grips with the story

★ What did Timothy volunteer to do in the class concert?
★ In the story that Mrs Bear made up, what did Joseph do about the scary cuddly bear that Mary found abandoned on the floor?
★ Why did Joseph, Mary and Jesus have to leave their home in Bethlehem?

Ways for children to express the story

★ Draw two pictures of an animal, one with a scary face and one with a kind face.
★ Make a list of five toys that young children could have had in the days when Jesus was born. Then make a list of five toys that are around now that certainly would not have been available then.

Helping children to own the story

★ Why do you think Timothy wanted so very much for a bear to be part of the Christmas story?
★ Why was it a good idea for Mary to call the bear Josephus?

Ways for children to live out the story

★ If you were asked to take part in a class concert, work out what you would do.

★ Which of your cuddly toys are most important to you? Why?

Index of Bible links

Old Testament Bible links

New Testament Bible links

Through the Year with Timothy Bear

24 five-minute stories for special days and seasons of the year

Meet Timothy Bear, who, together with his family and friends, finds himself at the centre of many adventures guaranteed to appeal to young children.

There is a story for all major special days throughout the year, as well as stories for each of the four seasons, making the material an ideal resource to teach biblical and moral truths to 5–7s. Each story includes a seasonal theme, PSHE links and Bible links, including the key passage in full. There is also follow-up material for the assembly or classroom, offering ways to help young children get to grips with the story, express the story, own the story and live out the story.

Ideal for use in collective worship and assemblies, PSHE and circle time, as an aid to the teaching of RE, or purely for enjoyment at story time.

ISBN 978 1 84101 394 7   £7.99
Available using the order form on page 127
or by visiting www.barnabasinschools.org.uk.

Easy Ways to Christmas Plays

Three complete plays with photocopiable permission

Vicki Howie

'Could you put on a nativity play?' These are words that many primary teachers and people who work with young children in preschool dread. What can be done with a group of 3–7 year olds who only have ten minutes to practise once a week?

Easy Ways to Christmas Plays contains three simple but effective Christmas plays that are fun for children, take little time to produce and yet have a clear Christian theme. Choose from three exciting themes: 'Come to my party!', 'The star who couldn't twinkle' and 'Shine your lights!' Each play contains:

★ Lots of mimes and actions, with speaking parts kept to a minimum.
★ Illustrated story to introduce the theme of the play to the children.
★ Useful 'countdown-to-playday' hints and activities.
★ Photocopiable scripts and activity sheets.
★ Simple stage plans to show where the characters stand.

ISBN 978 1 84101 017 5   £11.99
Available using the order form on page 127
or by visiting www.barnabasinschools.org.uk.

Easy Ways to Christmas Plays Volume 2

Three easy-to-perform plays for 3–7s

Vicki Howie

The festive season brings with it the wonderful opportunity to put on a simple nativity play with 3–7s. Following the success of Vicki Howie's ever-popular *Easy Ways to Christmas Plays*, this second book contains three brand new plays, each with a storyline that is woven around the Christmas story.

A five-week countdown begins with the play written as a delightful story for you to read to the children, continues with simple drama games that take the place of long rehearsals, and ends with an easy-to-do performance of the play. Choose from three exciting themes: 'The Advent calendar puzzle', 'What can I give him?' and 'Silent night'.

★ Easy preparation.
★ Lots of mimes and actions, with minimal speaking parts.
★ Five teaching sessions.
★ Off-the-peg activities.
★ Photocopy permission.

ISBN 978 1 84101 585 9   £11.99
Available using the order form on page 127
or by visiting www.barnabasinschools.org.uk.

Story Plays for Christmas

Three plays complete with stories and interactive activities

Vicki Howie

Here are three easy-to-stage Christmas plays to use with your lively group of 7–11 year olds. Each play is introduced with a story version, followed by suggestions for drama games and activities to explore the storyline. Read the story, have fun playing some drama games and then perform the play.

Choose from 'Have you seen Christmas?', 'The earth looks forward to Christmas' and 'Jump for joy!'

The plays are suitable for use in both school and church. The themes also present the opportunity to explore related topics, such as travel in biblical times, homelessness, the family and the planets. Includes photocopy permission on all scripts and performance poems.

ISBN 978 1 84101 400 5   £9.99
Available using the order form on page 127
or by visiting www.barnabasinschools.org.uk.

Nursery Rhyme Nativities

Three easy-to-perform plays for preschool
and early years learning

Brian Ogden

One of the biggest problems faced by those working with very young children at Christmas is how to involve pre-readers in the nativity story with the minimum of fuss and manageable preparation.

Here is an ideal solution that will delight teachers and parents alike. In this book, popular author Brian Ogden offers three very diverse plays—all of which can be performed with groups of any size. Each one tells the story of the first Christmas from a different perspective, using well-known nursery rhyme tunes to bring the storyline to life. Simple directions, costumes and props ensure that the children are given the opportunity to participate fully in the performance.

Includes photocopy permission.

ISBN 978 1 84101 236 0   £7.99
Available using the order form on page 127
or by visiting www.barnabasinschools.org.uk.

Assemblies for Autumn Festivals

27 ready-to-use ideas for festivals and feast days

Martin Cox

This book is packed with 27 tried-and-tested assembly ideas designed to resource both popular and lesser-known festivals in the first term of the new school year. The ideas fall under four main themes—Harvest, Saints, Remembrance and Advent—with at least two assemblies to choose from within each theme. Topics covered include St Matthew, Michaelmas, St Francis, St Luke, All Saints, Guy Fawkes, Christ the King, St Andrew and St Nicholas.

Each assembly includes key background information for the teacher, Bible links, creative ideas for introducing the theme, suggestions for visual aids and ideas for exploring the theme, including storytelling, drama, music, songs and prayers. Also, each assembly is backed up by a wealth of ideas for cross-curricular extension work in the classroom.

ISBN 978 1 84101 459 3   £7.99
Available using the order form on page 127
or by visiting www.barnabasinschools.org.uk.

Bethlehem Carols Unpacked

Creative ideas for Christmas carol services

Lucy Moore and Martyn Payne
with Bible*Lands*

This book uses eleven well-known carols that appear in the Bible*Lands* *Bethlehem Carol Sheet* to explore many different aspects of the Christmas message.

The resource is packed with interesting facts about the carols, extended Bible references and a wealth of all-age, practical, theme-based ideas for creative storytelling, poetry, prayers, drama and worship. The book is structured using a flexible pick-and-mix formula, designed to assist people at all levels of experience with the planning of a carol service. A special section for those under the age of five is also included, making the material suitable for toddler groups, preschool playgroups and pram services.

- Away in a manger
- God rest you merry, gentlemen
- Good King Wenceslas
- Hark! the herald-angels sing
- O come, all ye faithful
- O little town of Bethlehem
- Once in royal David's city
- Silent night
- The first Nowell
- We three kings
- While shepherds watched

ISBN 978 1 84101 534 7   £8.99
Available using the order form on page 127
or by visiting www.barnabasinschools.org.uk.

ORDERFORM

REF	TITLE	PRICE	QTY	TOTAL
394 7	Through the Year with Timothy Bear	£7.99		
017 5	Easy Ways to Christmas Plays	£11.99		
585 9	Easy Ways to Christmas Plays Volume 2	£11.99		
400 5	Story Plays for Christmas	£9.99		
236 0	Nursery Rhyme Nativities	£7.99		
459 3	Assemblies for Autumn Festivals	£7.99		
534 7	Bethlehem Carols Unpacked	£8.99		

POSTAGE AND PACKING CHARGES						
Order value	UK	Europe	Surface	Air Mail	Postage and packing	
£7.00 & under	£1.25	£3.00	£3.50	£5.50	Donation	
£7.10–£30.00	£2.25	£5.50	£6.50	£10.00	TOTAL	
Over £30.00	FREE	prices on request				

Name _____ Account Number _____

Address _____

_____ Postcode _____

Telephone Number_____

Email _____

Payment by: ❏ Cheque ❏ Mastercard ❏ Visa ❏ Postal Order ❏ Maestro

Card no ☐☐☐☐ ☐☐☐☐ ☐☐☐☐ ☐☐☐☐ ☐☐☐

Valid from ☐☐☐☐ Expires ☐☐☐☐ Issue no. ☐☐☐

Security code* ☐☐☐ *Last 3 digits on the reverse of the card. **ESSENTIAL IN ORDER TO PROCESS YOUR ORDER** Shaded boxes for Maestro use only

Signature _____ Date _____

All orders must be accompanied by the appropriate payment.

Please send your completed order form to:
BRF, 15 The Chambers, Vineyard, Abingdon OX14 3FE
Tel. 01865 319700 / Fax. 01865 319701 Email: enquiries@brf.org.uk

❏ Please send me further information about BRF publications.

Available from your local Christian bookshop.　　　　　　　BRF is a Registered Charity

Resourcing **Collective Worship and Assemblies, RE, Festivals, Drama** and **Art** in primary schools

- Barnabas RE Days—exploring Christianity creatively
- INSET
- Books and resources
- www.barnabasinschools.org.uk